BEES, WASPS
AND ANTS

BEES, WASPS AND ANTS

by J. Zahradník

HAMLYN

Text by Jiří Zahradník
Translated by Pavla Atherton
Illustrations by František Severa
Line drawings by František Severa and Jiří Zahradník
Photographs by Jiří Zahradník, Ladislav Havel, Jan Vaněk
and Vladimír Pokorný
Graphic design by Stanislav Seifert

Published by The Hamlyn Publishing Group Limited,
a division of Octopus Publishing Group
Michelin House, 81 Fulham Road, London SW3 6RB

ISBN 0 600 55804 5
Printed in Czechoslovakia by Svoboda
3/07/16/51-01

Contents

Foreword

Bees, wasps and allied insects (Hymenoptera) belong to an order which has been frequently unjustly ignored by nature lovers. Among the Hymenoptera we can find species equalling in beauty the more popular butterflies or beetles. Their lifestyle is no less interesting. In many species it is so unique as to be without parallel among other insects.

In no other order do so many species develop at the expense of other insects. Thus they play an important role in maintaining the balance of nature and are extremely important to man and his environment. In this respect they are irreplaceable.

There are about 15,000 species of Hymenoptera inhabiting central Europe; thus in terms of species numbers they are the richest order in its fauna. They appear with the first spring flowers and can be seen as late as November, and even exceptionally during winter. However, our knowledge of the lifestyle of many hundreds of species is still very scant.

During the years of working on the manuscript of this book I consulted a number of experts, both local and foreign, who very willingly loaned me material from their collections and helped to verify the identification of some species. Among many others I would like to name especially Professor Dr R. Folliot (Rennes) and Dr C. Plateaux (Paris), Dr J. Macek (National Museum, Prague), Z. Nigrin (The Orlické Museum, Choceň), and Dr Pavel Mikula (Ministry of Agriculture, Prague) and Mr Christopher O'Toole (Oxford).

A Brief Description of the Order Hymenoptera

Bees, wasps and allied insects (Hymenoptera) are a very extensive order showing much variety in general appearance, size, colour and lifestyle. One feature, however, is common to most of the species, namely two pairs of membranous wings. The scientific name of the order is derived from the Greek *hymen* (membrane) and *pteron* (wing).

Hymenoptera are mostly small and medium-sized species; nevertheless, some are extremely small — only tenths of a millimetre in length — while others are giants as long as 40 mm. Among the largest Hymenoptera in Europe are some members of the family Siricidae (Wood Wasps), Scoliidae, some Vespidae and some Ichneumonidae (Ichneumon Flies). Among the smallest ones are species of Scelionidae — at only 0.2 mm long they belong to some of the smallest known insects.

The colouring of many species is inconspicuous, with various shades of brown and browny-black predominating. The colouring of other species, however, can be very striking. The 'wasp pattern' of alternating bands of yellow and black is probably the best known. Nevertheless, this colour combination is found in many other groups, such as some Siricidae, Vespidae and Ichneumonidae and even in some solitary bees. Some Hymenoptera have a beautiful, bright metallic coloration, their bodies often bearing alternating areas of shiny metallic green, blue, fiery red or gold. The best known in this respect are the Chrysididae (Cuckoo Wasps), Torymidae and some of the other parasitic wasps. The bodies of some Hymenoptera are entirely hairless, while others are covered in groups or bands of tiny hairs (e. g. bumblebees, solitary bees, etc.). In many species the body surface is highly sculptured. The simplest ornamentations are circular or grain-shaped depressions called punctures, but in many cases there are also fine grooves, wrinkles, spines, ridges, keels or different combinations of these structures.

The order is not uniform in body structure. While all its members show a marked division of the body into head, thorax and abdomen, as in all insects, different ways of joining the thorax to the abdomen divide the order into two groups. The smaller group includes those species in which the abdomen is joined to the thorax along its full width (sub-order Symphyta — Sawflies). In the other, numerically much larger group (sub-order Apocrita), the thorax (mesosoma) and abdomen (metasoma) are often joined by a narrow petiole, formed from one or two of the abdominal segments.

The head is usually joined to the body by a narrow neck and is very mobile. It is most frequently angled downwards, at right angles to the longitudinal axis of the body. Less frequently it projects forwards. The frontal part of the head consists of the upper lip (labrum) which is attached dorsally to a shield-like structure (clypeus). This shield often

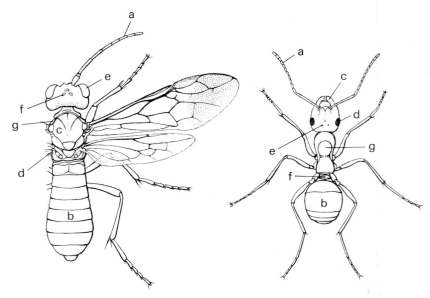

Diagram of Symphyta:
a — antenna, b — abdomen,
c — mesonotum, d — metanotum,
e — compound eye, f — ocellus,
g — pronotum.

Diagram of wingless Apocrita:
a — antenna, b — abdomen,
c — mandible, d — compound eye,
e — ocellus, f — petiole,
g — thorax.

carries features which are important for identification. Above the clypeus and between the eyes lies the forehead (frons), above this is the crown (vertex) and then the occiput. The neck opening (occipital foramen) is at the back of the head. Located behind the eyes are the temples (tempora) which run down under the eyes to form the cheeks (genae). There are two antennae, jointed onto the front of the head; on the sides of the head are two large compound eyes, while on the top or vertex are three simple eyes (ocelli) and in the front below the labrum are the mouthparts.

The antennae may be long, thin and threadlike, or short and thick, or sometimes club-shaped. The number of segments varies greatly. Antennae with 7—12 (13) segments predominate but some Ichneumonidae have as many as 70 antennal segments, while some Hymenoptera have as few as three segments. The first segment (scape) is usually thicker and larger. It is followed by a small segment called the pedicel. The remaining segments form the flagellum. In many Xyeloidea the third segment is the longest, while in some groups of small wasps, e.g. chalcids, the terminal segments of the antenna are joined together to form a club. The antennae of males and females often differ in number, shape, size and sometimes coloration of the segments.

The compound eyes, which are sometimes very large, are placed on the sides of the head. They are composed of variable numbers of tiny facets. Some species of Hymenoptera have only simple eyes. In females the compound eyes are usually further apart than in males.

Three simple eyes (ocelli), forming a triangle, are found on the vertex between the compound eyes.

The mouthparts come in many forms. Although mandibles are developed, they have not always retained their original chewing function. In females of many groups of the Hymenoptera they perform other tasks than the chewing of food. They serve mainly in nest-building, preparing food for the larvae, hunting prey, etc. Since most of the Hymenoptera live on vegetable juices or pollen grains, some mouthparts are adapted to licking and sucking of liquid food. The most perfect sucking mouthparts are found in the bee superfamily Apoidea, especially in worker honeybees and bumblebees, which have developed a long sucking tube and a hairy tongue.

The mesosoma or thorax is composed of three segments — prothorax, mesothorax and metathorax — which are not always clearly distinguishable. The mesothorax is the most developed segment and is connected with the development of the first pair of wings and their musculature.

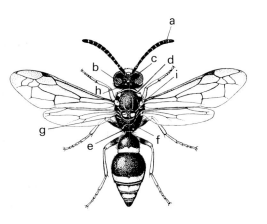

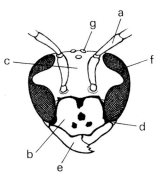

Diagram of winged Apocrita:
a — antenna, b — compound eye, c — simple eye (ocellus), d — pronotum, e — propodeum, f — metanotum, g — scutellum, h — vertex, i — tegula.

Diagram of a wasp's head:
a — antenna, b — clypeus, c — frons, d — gena, e — mandible, f — compound eye, g — ocellus.

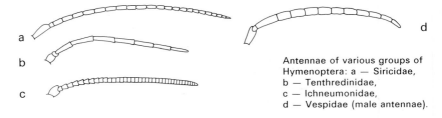

Antennae of various groups of
Hymenoptera: a — Siricidae,
b — Tenthredinidae,
c — Ichneumonidae,
d — Vespidae (male antennae).

The divisions of the thorax are most marked in the sawflies. The thorax is covered in a number of sclerites. These all have names but we shall acquaint ourselves with only the basic terms. At the front of the thorax the pronotum can be seen, especially on the sides. The middle part (mesonotum) is the most developed one, with its dorsal part forming the scutellum which often differs in colour. Behind this is the postscutellum which forms the prominent central part of the metanotum. In many Hymenoptera, e.g. the Ichneumonoidea, the divisions of the thorax are even more complicated.

Three pairs of legs and two pairs of wings are attached to the thorax.

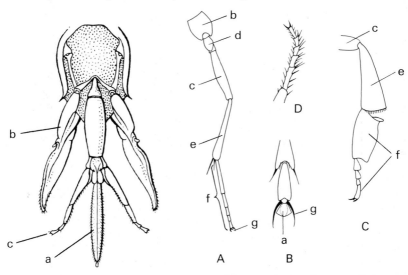

Mouthparts of a bee: a — tongue
(glossa), b — maxilla, c — labial palps.

Diagram of a leg: A — overall view,
B — close-up of end of foot,
C — modification of hind leg of worker
honeybee, D — tarsus of digging leg
(digger wasp), a — arolium, b — coxa,
c — femur, d — trochanter, e — tibia,
f — tarsus, g — claw (unguiculus).

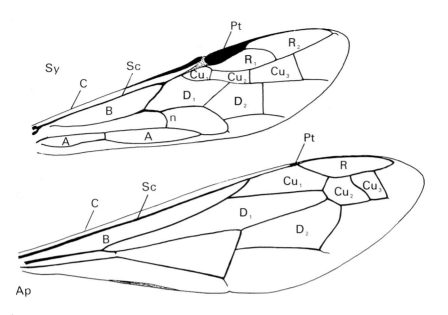

Important veins and cells in the fore-wing of sub-orders Symphyta (Sy) and Apocrita (Ap): A — anal cell (humeral, lanceolate), B — basal cell, C — costa, $Cu_1Cu_2Cu_3$ — cubital cells, D_1D_2 — discoidal cells, n — nervulus, Pt — pterostigma, R_1R_2 — radial cells, Sc — subcostal vein.

Each segment has a pair of legs but only the second and third segments have wings. The structure of the legs is the same as in other insect orders, each consisting of a coxa, a trochanter, a femur, a tibia and a tarsus.

From the distal end of the tibia project one or two thorn-like spurs; in some Symphyta there are additional (one to three) spines more proximal to these. The tarsus is usually composed of five parts but sometimes fewer. The first segment of the tarsus is called the metatarsus and the last segment is the pretarsus. The latter has two small claws (unguiculi), between which there is a single projection called the arolium, which is often lost in many groups.

Some of the legs are modified differently according to their function. For example, the forelegs are used as antennae cleaners and thus have an indentation for that purpose. The forelegs of female digger wasps are used for excavating the nest and so are comb-like. The most remarkable adaptation is the pollen-gathering and transporting mechanism found on the hind legs of female solitary bees, worker honeybees and bumblebees.

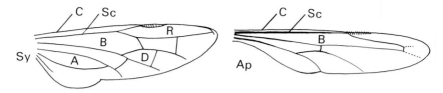

Important veins and cells in the hind wing of Symphyta (Sy) and Apocrita (Ap):
A — anal cell, B — basal cell, C — costa, D — discoidal cell, R — radial cell,
Sc — subcostal vein.

The wings are membranous, covered in fine hair, mostly translucent but in some species brownish or with violet reflections. The fore wings are longer than the hind wings; at the base of the former lies a horny scale (tegula). Both pairs of wings are strengthened by longitudinal veins and cross-veins. These veins form the venation which breaks up the wing area into a number of cells, all of which have separate names. At the front edge of the fore wing in most species there is a short dark area (pterostigma). The wing venation is most intricate and complete in the Symphyta. However, in some groups of parasitic Hymenoptera the wing venation is much reduced.

The arrangement of the veins as well as the shape and size of the cells are good identification features (see diagram of venation in some significant groups of Hymenoptera, p. 11).

Diagram of thorax from above: a — first pair of wings, b — second pair of wings, c — mesonotum, d — pronotum, e — propodeum, r — postscutellum, g — scutellum, h — tegula.

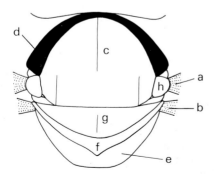

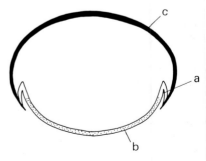

Cross-section of abdomen: a — pleurite, b — sternite, c — tergite. Only tergites and sternites show on the insect body; pleurites are hidden.

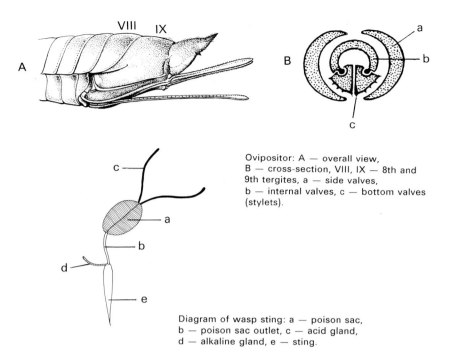

Ovipositor: A — overall view,
B — cross-section, VIII, IX — 8th and
9th tergites, a — side valves,
b — internal valves, c — bottom valves
(stylets).

Diagram of wasp sting: a — poison sac,
b — poison sac outlet, c — acid gland,
d — alkaline gland, e — sting.

At rest the wings are folded flat over the body; only in wasps of the families Leucospidae, Masaridae and Vespidae are they folded longitudinally. The front edge of the hind wing bears a row of tiny hooks, while the rear edge of the fore wing has a longitudinal furrow. The hooks fit into the furrow and unit fore and hind wings for flight.

Most species possess well-developed wings. However, in some Hymenoptera one of the sexes or castes is wingless (e.g. female Mutilloidea, worker ants, some parasitic wasps etc.) or shed their wings after a certain time (female ants after mating flight). In some species we find both winged and wingless individuals as well as ones with reduced wings (e.g. gall wasps).

The last of the body parts, the abdomen or metasoma, is the largest one. In theory it is composed of 11 segments but in practice only 6—8 or fewer can be seen. The single segments are ring-shaped and are connected by a membrane; the abdomen is thus very mobile. The dorsal part of each segment is called the tergite, the ventral part the sternite and the lateral joining part the pleurite. The metasoma contains the viscera and the copulatory organs. The female abdomen bears the egg-laying tube or ovipositor; in higher evolutionary groups this has been modified into the sting. The ovipositor may be short and thick, very long and needle-like, or totally concealed in the abdomen. The sting enables the insect to defend itself and to stun or kill its prey. It is hollow and connected to the poison gland. Its surface may be smooth or covered in tiny teeth. The sting of some Hymenoptera is quite painful (Mutilloidea, hornets, wasps, etc.); males never have a sting.

Reproduction and Development

Unlike some other insect orders, the Hymenoptera have several ways of reproducing.

The most common form of reproduction is bisexual. The fertilized female lays eggs which develop into larvae, these pass through a pupal stage and finally develop into the adults (imagines). Sometimes the females lay unfertilized eggs which nonetheless produce offspring; this is called parthenogenetic reproduction. Some Hymenoptera only reproduce parthenogenetically (so far no males have been discovered). There are also species in which parthenogenesis predominates but rare males are also found (e.g. in the very common Bedeguar Gall Wasp — *Diplolepis rosae*).

Some parasitic wasps reproduce in a very complicated and unusual way. The unfertilized egg divides into a large number of embryos, each of which gradually develops into an adult. This form of reproduction is called polyembryony.

Like many other higher insect orders, e.g. Coleoptera, Lepidoptera and Diptera, the Hymenoptera undergo complete metamorphosis. This means that the egg will after a variable period of time hatch out as a larva. The larva grows, casts off its skin several times and eventually changes into a pupa out of which the adult or imago will emerge.

The egg may have a smooth or roughly sculptured surface and its

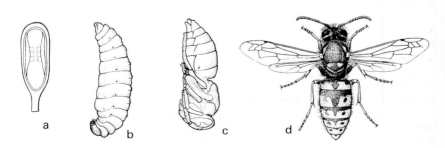

Development stages (Vespidae): a — egg, b — larva, c — pupa, d — adult.

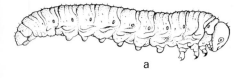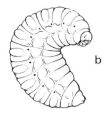

Two basic types of larvae: a — caterpillar-like larva,
b — apodous or grub-like larva.

size depends on both the size of the female and the number of eggs laid. This number depends further on the lifestyle of the species.

The shape of the larva varies according to its lifestyle. There are two basic types: one is a Symphyta-type larva which is caterpillar-like and usually has three pairs of thoracic legs, several pairs of pro-legs (abdominal legs) and one pair of stemmata. Lepidopteran caterpillars which resemble these larvae also have pro-legs but usually have several pairs of stemmata; the thoracic legs of caterpillars are thin, unlike the stronger legs of these hymenopteran larvae. The other type of hymenopteran larva is a legless (apodous), grub-shaped larva; this form is found in the Apocrita.

The larva is the only developmental stage that is capable of growth. The most opportune time for growth is directly after moulting when the old hard skin has been cast off and the new body cover is soft and flexible. The full-grown larva either stays in its habitat (e.g. larvae of bees, wasps, gall wasps, wood-boring wasps, etc.) or burrows into the ground or another hiding place. There it usually spins a cocoon around itself in which it passes months or even years as a so-called prepupa. The larvae of some Hymenoptera overwinter in this stage and only pupate in the spring. In some species the larvae do not spin cocoons but enclose themselves in a case of earth particles bonded together with saliva and in this they pupate.

The pupa is a typical so-called free pupa (pupa libera) in which the legs, antennae and wing cases are apparent. During this stage there is no active movement and most larval tissues are broken down and reassembled into adult tissues. There is no growth during the adult stage.

The full-grown insect or imago may stay in the cocoon for some time. Then it has to bite its way through the cocoon wall, the body of its host or the fibre of the leaf-gall. Males usually emerge before the females.

There is also a complicated and unusual way of reproducing called heterogeny where sexual and asexual generations alternate. This occurs in the gall wasps (Cynipoidea). One generation consists of agamous (asexual), i. e. unfertilized, females and their eggs hatch out to produce a sexual generation with both males and females. Both generations differ markedly in shape and lifestyle and develop in galls of different structure and size. The development takes place either on the same host plant (in the same or different part of it) or on different host plants (heteroecy).

Lifestyles

The Hymenoptera are terrestrial insects. Many species are warmth-loving and so inhabit open woodland and grassland localities, warm edges of forests, etc. They include both diurnal, crepuscular and nocturnal species. The latter are often attracted to light sources. Some species fly very heavily and reluctantly (sawflies); others spend a large part of their life flying and running. The great majority of species are solitary; however, some are social and live in large colonies.

Adult individuals are partial to flowering plants from which they obtain food — nectar, pollen and honeydew secreted by aphids. Although some species are predatory (e.g. ants, wasps), some of these also seek out sugary secretions.

Fertilized females lay their eggs in a wide variety of places. Sawflies and parasitic Hymenoptera use an egg-laying tube or ovipositor. The females instinctively care for the future generation at least by laying their eggs in places where the larvae will find enough food. Often they are laid in vegetable matter (e.g. Tenthredinoidea, Cynipoidea), on the body of another insect or arthropod or inside the body of another insect (e.g. ichneumons, braconids, chalcids, etc.). When the egg is laid on the body of the host and the larva develops on the surface of it, we call it ectoparasitism. When it is injected into the tissues of the host, inside which the development takes place, it is called endoparasitism. Some species of the Hymenoptera insert their eggs into the larvae or pupae of members of their own order (e.g. ichneumons into the larvae of wood wasps). Some Polistinae and cuckoo bees do not make a nest or care for their offspring; instead, their offspring develop in the nests of related species. Ants lay their eggs in cells and tunnels, honeybees, bumblebees and social wasps in prepared combs made of wax or paper-like pulp.

The larvae may be either herbivorous or carnivorous. The caterpillar-like larvae of sawflies are usually herbivorous. They live most often on leaves, the tissue of which provides them with sufficient nourishment. The larvae of some species actually live inside the leaf tissue. Communally living larvae often spin a silk canopy around themselves which protects them from their enemies. Grub-like, legless larvae are not able to move actively and this determines their living and feeding habits. This form of larva occurs most frequently in predatory species. The larvae of many species spend all their lives on the body of a larva (or pupa) of another insect species, usually a lepidopteran or beetle, or inside its body tissues. In both cases they slowly digest their host. The larvae of communally living Hymenoptera are not able to feed themselves and are dependent on the care of worker individuals (wasps, honeybees, bumblebees, ants). The presence of the larvae of herbivorous gall wasps causes the host plant to produce excessive tissue, creating a gall in which the wasp develops.

Most Hymenoptera produce only a single generation in the course of a year. In parasitic species there may be two or more generations, while in some species one generation may take longer than a year to complete its development.

Caring for the Offspring

Many species, indeed whole groups of species of Hymenoptera, have a well-developed ability to care for their offspring. The caring efforts of the females can best be illustrated by an example. A very simple way of providing for the next generation occurs in various small chalcids. The parasitic adult chalcid wasp finds a victim — a host, most often the larva of another insect or, perhaps, an aphid or scale insect. It lays its egg on the surface of the host's body or inside its tissue and looks after its offspring no further. After a short time, the chalcid larva hatches and finds an ample supply of suitable food ready and waiting. It then lives either on the surface or inside its host and slowly digests the host's internal tissues. Only after the host has been largely or entirely consumed does the larva pupate.

Parental care is highly developed in many female Hymenoptera. In digger wasps (Sphecidae), the female not only digs a nest for her offspring but also provides a sufficient quantity of suitable food, usually the larvae of other insects or spiders. The digger wasp cannot bury its victim alive in the nest as it would escape. Neither can it kill it, otherwise the body would soon decay in the heat of the summer. The digger wasp makes its prey into something we could call an insect preserve — it paralyses the victim by injecting venom with its sting. The effect of the venom is long-lasting and so perfect that the victim is rendered immobile, but remains alive. The digger wasp sometimes bites the legs off the prey. Thus the paralysed victim does not decay and its body provides enough food for the digger wasp larva to complete its development. Similarly, the females of the Scolioidea paralyse the larvae of some scarabaeid beetles (*Oryctes nasicornis,* Rose Chafer, etc.) before they lay their eggs, but do not construct nests. Instead, they burrow into the soil where the larvae live and sting them before laying an egg.

An even more perfect way of caring for the young can be observed in all the social species of Hymenoptera. The larvae of wasps, honeybees, bumblebees and ants are unable to feed themselves at any stage from birth till they are fully grown and so they are entirely dependent on the care of the workers who continually feed them.

The Creators of the First Colonies on Earth

Insect colonies are spoken of and written about as a matter of course and no-one seems to balk at the unusual connection of the words 'insect' and 'colony'. We have a general idea of insect colonies but there is still much to be discovered.

Social insects are found in two distantly related orders: the Hymenoptera and the Isoptera (termites). The basic difference between them is their way of metamorphosis. The Hymenoptera are one of the insect orders which undergo complete metamorphosis, while the termites, which are very closely related to cockroaches, undergo incomplete metamorphosis. In spite of this fundamental difference, the termite remains to the layman just 'another sort of ant'. We are seduced into this view by the termites' way of life, which is very similar to that of the ants. On the European continent, termites are represented by very few species and the architecture of their European colonies — termite nests — is of very little interest. European termites remain concealed from view and their existence is usually discovered only when the wooden objects or buildings, in which they have settled and reared a number of generations, fall apart. In tropical regions, however, termite nests are very diverse and in many places are a characteristic part of the landscape.

Since early times scientists and writers have been fascinated by colonial insects. They tried to look into their secret lives and understand their unceasing activity. The result has been many large volumes, some good and some not so good, some scientifically sound and some full of imagination. Among the researchers in social insects there are people of the calibre of D. V. Alford, K. Escherich, W. Goetsch, K. Gösswald, W. V. Harris, I. Hrdý, I. Chalifman, R. Chauvin, P. P. and M. W. Larson, E. O. Wilson, C. D. Michener and others. Professor Karl von Frisch and his team were awarded the Nobel Prize for their excellent research into social insects, especially the honeybee. Not only scientists but also popular science and fiction writers have been attracted to the mysteries of insect colonies. For example, M. Maeterlinck's way of writing about them is romantic and mystically thrilling.

We like to compare life in human society with that of other creatures. We do, however, tend to compare the incomparable. We try to find similarities between the insect social community and the human community, although we already know that the common denominator — the community — has a different meaning and different laws in each case.

The insect colony is instinctively based, the ability to live communally is carried on from generation to generation without change. The insect colony often consists of only one very large 'family' headed always by the mother — queen. Seen through human eyes, it is a matriarchy. In the insect colony three different groups of inhabitants (castes) live together in a hierarchy. They look similar but there are differences in size, the arrangement and development (or disappearance) of certain physical features and of course different lifestyles. Apart from the mother — queen ($\female$), and possibly several other mothers, the colony also comprises workers ($\female$), which are imperfectly developed females. Males ($\male$) only appear at a certain time. There are differences not only between members of different castes but also between individuals belonging to the same caste. For example, some ant workers have large heads and strong mandibles and are usually (though not always correctly) called soldiers. The queen can be the real mother of the whole family — all the 'daughters' and 'sons'. This occurs where there is only one queen in the whole colony, e.g. in wasps, bumblebees and honeybees. Where there is more than one queen in the nest, as in some ant and wasp species, the situation is more complicated. The queens may (but need not) be related, and so may their offspring. However, there is a high degree of mutual tolerance. Wasp, bee and ant colonies are roughly estimated by experts to be about 100 million years old; termite colonies are apparently even older. All those years ago, bees and bumblebees knew how to 'produce' wax and social wasps knew how to build their nests from paper-like material. Their building art is always the same, always perfect, it neither dies out nor does it develop. Maybe here and there they may make a 'short-cut' when instead of wood chips, wasps collect a scrap of newspaper or a granule of polystyrene to use in building their nest. They are the grand-masters of their craft. They always have enough building materials and use them with maximum economy and speed. They have no time to waste — their lifespan is limited and the tasks they have to fulfil are very many.

The changelessness and ruthlessness of the laws of an insect colony apply also to its end. This comes very soon — in wasps and bumblebees in the same year as the colony was founded. The old queen, the workers and the males die; only the females born and fertilized at the end of the summer survive the winter in some hideaway. Only the colonies of ants, halictid bees, honeybees and a few kinds of wasps persist for several years.

Having considered the basics of insect colonies, let us take a look at an example of the establishment and defence of such an insect colony and the way it is terminated. We shall take as an example a wasp colony which is really a paragon of a perfect colony. In comparison, the honeybee community is strongly influenced by man, who provides perfect housing for the bees, frames in which to build their honeycombs and even food supplements in winter. Bumblebee and ant colonies lack the intricacy and neatness of the wasp colony.

The colonies of all wasp species living in the temperate zone exist only during a certain part of the plant growth cycle; some of them die out at the end of the summer, while the vegetation is still flourishing. Their maximum duration is about six months. Every colony is founded in the spring by a queen which has survived the winter in hibernation. Some species found their nests near the place they were born and overwintered but none use the previous year's nests. The fact that wasps found and build their nests anew every year is little known. It is a popular misconception that wasps' and bumblebees' colonies last for several years, as do those of honeybees and ants.

Social, paper-making wasps, honeybees and potter wasps (which bring up their larvae in neat little clay pots reminiscent of Greek amphorae) are among the best and undoubtedly most diligent architects and builders of the insect world. Their nests are characterized by an incredible regularity, neatness and efficiency. Moreover, when we realize that most species build their nests in pitch darkness, we have to admit we are witnessing something exceptional. The layman may claim that architecture is the prerogative of man alone, but this is not so. Many of the six-legged inhabitants of this Earth show good evidence of their building abilities, fixed in their nervous systems by heredity.

All European social wasps make their nests out of a paper-like material. They prepare it relatively easily and quickly from wood chips mixed with saliva. They carry it in a ball to the nest, spread it out in a suitable place and fly off again for more material. They mostly use only a certain quality of wood; to be more exact, wood in a certain stage of ageing and decay. Some wasps gather only old, rotting wood, others scrape off splinters from dry tree trunks and beams or dry branches. Only exceptionally do they chew off living wood. The material used influences not only the resulting colour but also the strength of the nest. Some wasps' nests are yellowish (common wasps, hornets), others are grey (most of our species). During the building the wasps may even recycle the paper-like material of their own nest but this only occurs at the height of the season, when they make various adjustments to the nest.

Choosing the place to build a nest and laying its foundations is a very important event for the queen wasp. She does not choose the place at random but examines the landscape carefully before making a decision. In spite of all the care expended on these preparations, the place may not be suitable and the nest either dies out or the wasps have to seek an emergency solution. The queen herself builds only a small part of the nest — first the stalk from which the nest will hang, then the first few cells and a part of the protective wrapping enclosing them. These cells form the basis of the topmost comb (the nest is suspended and the wasps build from top to bottom, not vice versa). All the cells in the comb have their open end downwards. The female glues a single egg in each cell. The larvae soon hatch out and then the queen has another duty — feeding. Up until now she has only had to look after her own nourishment but now she has to fly out to hunt various insects, mainly flies and caterpillars, which she feeds to the larvae. The larvae are not able to provide their own food because they cannot leave their cells. Initially they are stuck to the cells so they will not fall out. Very rapidly they grow large and fat and soon fit so tightly into their cells that it is impossible for them to fall out. Each now spins a silken lid for its cell, pupates inside and shortly appears as one of the first workers — the future helpers of the queen. It is tempting to say 'slaves' because the workers know nothing but tireless work for the good of the community. They take over all the queen's duties apart from the laying of eggs. This latter remains the queen's sole function. The workers continue to build other combs which are, like the first one, horizontal. The combs are connected by a central stalk and lateral supports further strengthen the whole nest. As well as the smaller cells for the workers,

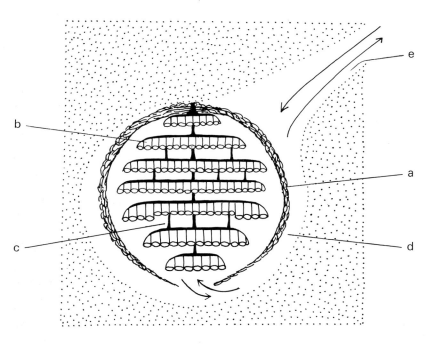

Diagram of underground wasps' nest: (arrows indicate wasps flying in and out)
a — covering, b — comb, c — strengthening bars, d — air space, e — entrance tunnel.

wider cells for the males and females — future queens — are built at a certain time. Among the builders' duties are also the widening of the nest space and the building of the protective covering round the combs. The workers also feed the larvae and the queen and remove refuse from the nest. In very hot weather they cool down the nest by vibrating their wings and spraying water around. In some species the nest entrance is protected by guards which repel all intruders; they distinguish them by their smell. All the inhabitants of a nest share the colony odour; they are accustomed to each other's smell and recognize the inhabitants of other nests by their different odour.

The life of the nest runs for the most part routinely. The queen usually does not leave the nest once workers are present. If she died, it would mean a premature end of the colony. At the height of summer and towards its end females and males start hatching out in the nest. This is the climax of its development. Now the end of the colony is approaching. The limited life expectancy of a wasp colony is due to a number of causes. One of them is lack of food, for wasps are not able to lay in winter supplies; furthermore the workers are not capable of surviving the winter. Only in tropical regions can the wasp colony last over several years because of the more favourable climatic conditions, which guarantee enough food for the larvae. Interestingly, our two most common wasps — *Vespula vulgaris* and *V. germanica* — have been observed, when introduced into tropical habitats, to found colonies of not one but several years' duration.

The wasp colony usually ends naturally but may come to a violent end while it is still flourishing (through destruction by man or the death of the queen). The queen's premature death, whether natural or violent, causes the gradual death of the colony. In such a case some of the workers start to lay eggs but as these are infertile, only males will hatch. The colony will continue for some time but its end is inevitable. The colony can be endangered or gradually die out when the queen does not select a suitable place for the nest and it becomes clear during nest building that it cannot be widened. The wasps then leave the nest or build another in the immediate vicinity, sometimes joined to the original one. The arrival of a cuckoo wasp means total extinction of the original inhabitants of the nest, even though the colony appears to survive. The cuckoo wasp kills the original queen, takes over the nest, lays its eggs there and its offspring are brought up by the original queen's workers.

The worst calamity that can befall the wasp colony is man's interference. He may use insecticide to destroy the nest. Digging operations may seriously damage the nest and the queen may survive or be killed. If the queen survives, there is a chance of reviving the nest. The remaining workers congregate on the wrecked combs and try to build new cells, rebuild damaged combs and continue to feed the surviving larvae. Each newly hatched worker is a reinforcement for the whole colony. However, if the workers are destroyed by insecticide and the queen dies, the life of the whole colony comes to an end.

In the temperate zone, the autumn signals the inevitable natural end of the wasp community. It has been a long time coming. I have often observed the workers of *Vespula* and hornets in October and sometimes on sunny days in November, carrying live larvae out of the nest and dumping them on the ground outside, thus causing their death. The reason for this is obviously that at the height of the summer (in late summer in some species) mostly males and females are hatching out in the nest and only very few workers. The lack of workers adversely affects the supply of food for the larvae. As the workers cannot manage to feed all the larvae or give them enough food, the larvae starve and lose weight. The cells they sit in become too large for them and the larvae fall out of them on to the roof of the comb underneath. To the worker they are then rubbish, and so they are grasped in the mandibles and carried outside. Many larvae die of starvation in the nest at the time when no more workers are available to bring food into the nest. Shortly after this the workers and males die, the young queens find a winter refuge in which to hibernate and the nest collapses because the paper-like mass cannot last long in the soil. When the autumn rains come, the water soaks into the underground nest, a greenish-grey mould appears on it and the combs quickly disintegrate. I have observed a mouldy coating on a dug-up nest of the common wasp as early as September 30th, even while there were still several live workers and young females in it. Only the nests built under the eaves or in the lofts of houses or holiday homes are more durable. Even they, though, will in time disintegrate through the influence of changing temperatures and humidity.

The building of the wasps' combs and the general arrangement of the whole wasps' domed nest is one of nature's many remarkable creations. Have a look sometime at a deserted, empty wasp or hornet nest. There is a unique regularity in its shape; each cell exactly like the next, regular hexagons closely grouped together. Bear in mind that both the queen and the workers built these combs in total darkness and in a limited, narrow space. The workers had never learned how to do it, they simply started building and they built with the maximum precision and efficiency. So many questions present themselves: how did the wasp arrive at this cell arrangement, how does it maintain their regular hexagonal shape? Generations follow upon generations and the work goes on without error. The workers are little artists. They continue the work started by their predecessors with the same precision and reliability. Modern research has analysed and described in detail the behavioural sequences involved in the construction of massed hexagonal cells.

Insect 'Cuckoos'
and Other Cohabitants of Insect Colonies

Cuckoos occur not only among birds but also among insects; probably the best known ones are found in the nests of social insects. These are the pseudo-wasps and pseudo-bumblebees; incapable of founding a nest of their own or bringing up their own offspring, they colonize the nest of a related social insect species for this purpose. This occupation takes different forms in different species but the aim is the same: to ensure the feeding and upbringing of one insect's future generation at another's expense.

Let us first look at the cuckoo wasps. They have no workers to feed the larvae and build the nest. However, the cuckoo wasp still has to ensure the survival of her offspring. The female (the future queen) ensures her own future and that of her colony as follows: first she finds a nest of the future host species. There have to be workers in it, or at least their larvae and pupae about to hatch out. The 'cuckoo' wasp needs them to bring up its own young. A scent or pheromone similar to those of the host wasps apparently enable her to enter their nest with impunity. This is the only possible explanation for the fact that the wasps do not kill her immediately as she attempts to enter. As soon as the cuckoo wasp penetrates the nest, she usually kills the queen and settles in her place. From that moment the nest belongs to her. She immediately makes a start on her only task — egg-laying. The workers which were in the nest or are still hatching serve the cuckoo wasp. They begin to feed and look after all its offspring as thoroughly as they would have done for members of their own species. Gradually the intruder's offspring become the majority in the colony and the original inhabitants die out. In any case, towards the autumn they are not needed any longer because this occupied colony also dies out before the arrival of winter. Only fertilized females survive the winter and next spring they found a new colony. The occupation of a *Polistes* nest by a pseudo-*Polistes* runs along similar lines. The intruder kills or chases out the queen and occupies the nest. Sometimes this happens a little less violently. There is a skirmish, the stronger and larger pseudo-*Polistes* wins but the former queen remains in the nest. She ceases to be the queen and becomes a worker, posing a threat no more since she no longer lays eggs. There is a serious danger to the aggressors, though: if they occupy all the nests and destroy their inhabitants, there will be no-one to take care of their offspring in the next season and the pseudo-*Polistes* becomes extinct in that locality.

How did these parasitic social species originate? Various reasons have led to the theory that the 'cuckoo' wasps have developed over a long period from non-parasitic species which gradually lost the ability to live communally.

The bumblebees (*Bombus* spp.) also have their 'cuckoos' — the very similar-looking cuckoo-bees (*Psithyrus* spp.). The cuckoo-bees also lack workers and they let a related (and similar) bumblebee species bring up their larvae. We do not know as much about their life histories as we would like to. Some species of cuckoo-bee appear to be more tolerant than others: there are often both queens living in the same nest. The real ruler, of course, is the cuckoo-bee queen, while the original one remains there more or less on sufferance, with her eggs being eaten by the cuckoo female. But in some species the intruding female *Psithyrus* kills the colony's queen.

A certain similarity with 'cuckoos' occurs in some ants but their life differs from that of the 'cuckoo' wasps and cuckoo-bees. Although the queen 'cuckoo' ants of some species found their new colonies as violently as the 'cuckoo' wasps or cuckoo-bees, i.e. by breaking into a nest of a different species, their first offspring are workers and only after a certain period do the males and females appear. The first workers, however, need another individual to bring them up instead of their own mother. A good example is the well-known Wood Ant (*Formica rufa*). The fertilized female of the Wood Ant founds a new colony usually in a nest of a different ant species, often *Formica fusca*. If the nest happens to have no queen at the time, the whole affair takes place in peace. If there is a native queen present, the situation is slightly more complicated. There is then no other option but to fight. The weaker *F. fusca* queen is defeated and she is usurped by the Wood Ant queen. From that moment onwards the *F. fusca* colony goes into a slow decline. At the beginning the life in the anthill goes on as before but gradually more and more Wood Ant workers appear and take over all the duties — extend the nest, feed the larvae and their queen. The *Formica fusca* workers are fewer and fewer, until they disappear completely and their original nest becomes a pure Wood Ant colony.

The establishment of a nest can be even more complicated than in *Formica rufa*. The queen of that species is not capable of founding a nest and bringing up workers but her offspring are able to perform all the functions necessary for the colony to continue. There are ants, though, whose females not only cannot found their own colonies or feed their own larvae, but also must have slaves to attend to all their needs; these slaves greatly outnumber them in the nest. An example of such a slave-maker is *Polyergus rufescens*. It is aggressive and loots the colonies of other ant species for worker pupae, which eventually become slaves.

Apart from the 'cuckoos', insect colonies are inhabited by dozens of other insect species. Their relationships with their hosts are very varied and sometimes very strange. The largest numbers of cohabitants and the greatest variety of species are found in ant colonies. They include species which provide sweet food for the ants (e.g. aphids), but also intruders which prey on the young or ailing members of the host species. Experts divide all ant cohabitants into three large groups and each group has a name. There are the symphiles — the species encouraged by the ants, the synoeketes — species tolerated by the ants, and the synechthrans — scavenging and predatory species. Most of the members of each category are beetles, especially the Staphylinidae. Their life in the dark corridors of the anthills alone could provide material for a very thick tome indeed!

How Many Species of Hymenoptera Are There?

The question of how many species of Hymenoptera exist and how many remain undiscovered is often posed. I shall quote some data gathered by experts; it will become apparent how little we know of this important insect group.

According to Professor Bernard in Grassé's extensive compendium 'Traité de Zoologie' (1951), the number of described species of Hymenoptera is about 280,000 and the probable overall number of species is estimated at around one million. In contrast, Professor Kaestner's estimate in the excellent textbook 'Lehrbuch der Zoologie' (1975) is much more cautious and apparently more realistic. Kaestner suggests about 100,000 described species. B. Grzimek arrives at a similar figure in his 'Grzimeks Tierleben', an extensive 13-volume work also published in 1975.

As regards the number of Hymenoptera living in central Europe, the figures at our disposal are more exact. These amount to some 15,000 species. For the whole of Europe the estimated figure is 45,000. The beetles — the best researched of insect orders — take first place in the world with some 350,000 species. However, in the fauna of central Europe the beetles are in second place, far behind the Hymenoptera, and this situation is likely to remain. Interestingly, the number of Diptera, (two-winged flies), an order neglected until recently, is increasing and we cannot exclude the possibility of it equalling or even overtaking the number of beetles in central Europe.

The Importance of Hymenoptera to Man

Many of us underestimate the importance of Hymenoptera to man. And yet Hymenoptera are most important insects in several respects.

Firstly, they are pollinators. In this role they are irreplaceable and indispensable. The honeybee, solitary bees and bumblebees (and to a lesser extent the members of other groups) are responsible for most of the pollination of insect-pollinated plants. Without their tireless activity fruit trees would not bear fruit and many plants would not produce seed. The pollen adheres to the hairy body of the insect which then transfers it from one flower to the stigma of another. Bees and their relatives, however, do not fly from flower to flower just to pollinate them. They are attracted by the nectar and the pollen — the main food of many Hymenoptera. With regard to the predatory hymenopteran species, both sexes enjoy the food the flowers offer; the females catch insect prey as food for their larvae and may occasionally feed on the body fluids of the prey. Bees of many species make paste from pollen and nectar for their larvae. The female prepares either an ample supply of it in advance (in solitary species) or a small amount at the beginning and then the workers take over the care of the larvae (in bumblebees).

Man makes use of the simple fact that honeybees carry the nectar into their hives to convert into honey as a food supply for the inhabitants; he then takes the honey away from them. Making honey is a laborious process. When you buy a pound jar of honey, it is difficult to realize that to 'produce' this amount the bees had to visit and suck the nectar from about three million red clover flowers, two-and-a-half million vetch flowers or over three quarters of a million pseudo-acacia flowers. Honey is a high-quality food. It is very easily digestible, because the sugars it contains do not have to be digested but are absorbed straight from the alimentary tract. Honey is also well known for its anti-bacterial properties. The bee transforms the nectar and other sugary substances into honey through complicated biochemical processes in her body. The material is gradually dehydrated and fermented into simple sugars — glucose and fructose. The nectar is thickened and the sugar transformed in the honeypouch of the foraging workers, which then hand it over to the young bees in the hive for further processing. These thicken it further until it contains no more than 20 per cent water. The honey is then deposited in cells in the honeycomb and sealed with a wax cap.

Wax is another useful product of honeybees. It is exuded from the wax-producing glands in the abdomen of workers and used as a building material. Chemically it is a wax of the highest quality. The most recently formed honeycomb contains the highest percentage of wax (up to 98 per cent). The older honeycombs contain various additives and the proportion of wax is lower. Pure wax is produced by melting down the honeycombs and is used for making honeycomb partitions and in dentistry, cosmetics, etc.

Propolis or bee-glue is a mixture of wax and various resins from the buds of poplars, firs, horse-chestnuts and other trees. Bees use it for filling in cracks in the walls of the hive. Because of its bactericidal and fungicidal properties it is beginning to have applications in medicine.

Pollen also can be used by man and is a good source of vitamins and several other important substances.

Bee poison is excreted from the poison gland. Together with other substances it forms the liquid the bee injects through her sting.The bee poison affects different species in different ways. It can cause instant death, e.g. to various Diptera. The bee's sting can also endanger larger animals. It is well known that some people are allergic to it. Bee poison is an important raw material in the preparation of medicine for the treatment of rheumatic illnesses, some allergies, etc.

Royal jelly is produced in the hypopharyngeal gland of young bees. It is a very nourishing and easily digestible protein-like substance used to feed the larvae of future queens during the whole time of their development. The other larvae only receive it during their first three days. Royal jelly is also consumed by the queen. It has attracted a lot of research interest. Its antibiotic properties and its chemical composition are utilized in the pharmaceutical industry in the production of medicines for the treatment of venous, pulmonary and other illnesses. Royal jelly is also used in a number of cosmetic preparations for its alleged conditioning and regenerative qualities.

Many species of Hymenoptera act as natural pest controllers. Thousands of species of ichneumons and braconids are parasitic on various insects — very often the pests of our woods, fields and gardens. Exceptionally important are the tiny chalcids whose larvae develop as ectoparasites or endoparasites on other insects. They are very numerous but in spite of living in our gardens, woods and fields they are rarely seen. We can, however, rear them at home from various aphids, scale insects and other insects. They attack an immense number of pests which they limit to a large extent, until man upsets the natural balance by the use of insecticides. The negative effects of such interference are well known by now but only the future will show how much harm has been done to nature by the excessive use of these chemicals. The developed countries are therefore increasingly trying to apply biological methods of pest control, making use of the fact that many species of tiny wasps feed on the larval stage of various pests. These parasitic species are cultivated in insectaries on a large scale and during periods of great pest infestation are artificially introduced over large areas. Not even oceans stand in the way of biological pest control methods. These parasites have been introduced from North America to Europe and vice versa. Modern science is constantly exploring the life of these tiny useful insects and trying to use them as efficiently as possible in fighting pests. Biological control is not always used by itself but an integrated approach has also been tried (not always successfully), using both insects and insecticides.

There are, however, some pest species among the Hymenoptera themselves (e.g. the larvae of some sawflies) but, on balance, the negative effect of these pests is quite negligible.

A Systematic Summary of the Order Hymenoptera

(The star* after family name means that one of its species is considered more fully in the illustrated part of this book.)

1st Sub-order: Symphyta
Evolutionally the oldest of the Hymenoptera whose abdomen is joined to the thorax along its whole width and height. Males and females differ in shape and colour of body, shape of antennae, etc. Wings always have well-developed venation. They are reluctant, heavy and sometimes noisy fliers. Females have ovipositors of varying length. The larvae are similar to the caterpillars of Lepidoptera und usually have thoracic legs and abdominal prolegs.

There are 6 European super-families:

Super-family: Xyeloidea. These are evolutionally very old. The imagines are tiny, only several millimetres long. The 12-segmented antennae are unusually shaped: the last 9 segments are very short and weak. The imagines are rare and found in spring, mostly in young pine woods. Family: Xyelidae

Super-family: Megalodontoidea. Most imagines have a broad head and a distinct ridge along the sides of the abdomen. The antennae are multi-segmented. The wings can be yellowish or dark. The larvae feed on vegetable tissue; some species are pests.
Families: Megalodontidae, Pamphiliidae* (Web-spinning and Leaf-rolling Sawflies)

Super-family: Siricoidea. These are large with cylindrical bodies and are noisy fliers. The fore wing has either two (Xiphydriidae) or three (Siricidae) cubital cells. The length of the ovipositor in the female is variable. The larvae develop in the wood of coniferous and deciduous trees and are parasitized by several large ichneumonids.
Families: Siricidae* (Horntails or Wood Wasps), Xiphydriidae*.

Super-family: Orussoidea. These are tiny species, only several mm long, with 11-segmented antennae. They have only one closed cubital

cell on the fore wing. The ovipositor of the female is needle-like. The larvae are parasitic on larvae of wood-boring beetles.
Family: Orussidae.

Super-family: Cephoidea. These tiny, slim species have the abdomen sometimes laterally compressed. The larvae have poorly developed legs and live on various plants.
Family: Cephidae (Stem Sawflies).

Super-family: Tenthredinoidea (Sawflies). The imagines are of various sizes and colours, often dark, yellowish or metallic. The antennae have a variable number of segments — at least 3 (Argidae), very often 9 (Tenthredinidae), sometimes more than 18 (Diprionidae). In some the antennae are club-like (Cimbicidae). This is the super-family with the most species and many of them are very difficult to identify.
Families: Argidae*, Blasticotomidae, Cimbicidae*, Diprionidae*, Tenthredinidae* (Typical Sawflies).

2nd Sub-order: Apocrita

The junction between meso- and metasoma is clearly marked and often petiolate. The ovipositor of the female either protrudes freely or is retracted (Terebrantes) or converted into a sting (Aculeata) for the defence of the individual and also for paralysing prey. The larvae are without legs.

Many groups are noted for their ability to care for their offspring. Some species form colonies; many are beneficial as parasites of various pests. There are 18 super-families in Europe. The classification, however, requires revision and some super-families, e.g. Sapygoidea and Mutilloidea are probably best placed in a more broadly defined Vespoidea.

Super-family: Trigonaloidea. The black imagines have spotty wings and resemble tiny wasps. The antennae have about 24 segments. The development is complicated as the larvae are hyper-parasitoids, i.e. parasitoids of other parasitoids.
Family: Trigonalidae.

Super-family: Ichneumonoidea. A large group including tiny, medium-sized and large species (in Europe there are several thousand species) which are often very difficult to identify. The colouring can be dark and inconspicuous or bright. The antennae usually have more than 16 segments. An important identifying feature is a so-called areole on the fore wing (see page 38, ref. 30(31) — a). Some species are armed with a long ovipositor. They are mostly parasitic on insect or other arthropods' larvae and pupae. Mostly useful species.

Families: Aphidiidae, Ichneumonidae* (Ichneumon Flies), Braconidae*, Agriotypidae.

Super-family: Stephanoidea. These are widespread in Africa, with only a few European species.
Family: Stephaniidae.

Super-family: Evanoidea. Very variable in shape, these insects have a common denominator — a small, laterally compressed abdomen with a petiole joining the thorax high above the coxa.
Families: Evaniidae, Gasteruptiidae, Aulacidae.

Super-family: Cynipoidea. These are tiny species, only several mm long; they are inconspicuous, dark brown, yellow-brown to black. The wings have a large, slanted radial cell and no pterostigma. The antennae are 13—19-segmented and the abdomen is laterally compressed. Cynipoidea feed on plants or are parasitic on insects. Along with the gall-forming species there are the inquilines (also Cynipoidea) — species which do not make their own gall but develop in that of another species. Gall-forming species have a complicated development.
Families: Cynipidae* (Gall Wasps), Ibaliidae, Eucoilidae, Figitidae.

Super-family: Chalcidoidea. A super-family of tiny, 2—3 mm long and larger species. The venation is much reduced: the sub-costal vein is partly parallel to the wing edge, the radial short and button-like. Many species have a beautiful metallic colouring. The larvae live as parasites in various insects, e.g. aphids, scale insects, etc. They are important in biological pest control. Some species are raised artificially and introduced in pest-infested areas.
Families: Chalcididae (Chalcids), Leucospidae, Perilampidae, Eucharitidae, Pteromalidae, Eupelmidae, Encyrtidae, Eurytomidae, Torymidae*, Ormyridae, Agaonidae, Tetracampidae, Eulophidae, Elasmidae, Aphelinidae*, Trichogrammatidae, Signiphoridae, Mymaridae.

Super-family: Proctotrupoidea. These are mostly tiny (0.2—5 mm, rarely larger) black or brown species with no metallic sheen. The wing venation is reduced. The larvae are parasitic on various insects.
Families: Heloridae, Proctotrupidae, Diapriidae, Scelionidae, Serphitidae, Platygastridae.

Super-family: Ceraphronoidea. These are very tiny (0.5—4 mm) and mostly dark-coloured. The pterostigma is large in some species. So far they are mostly unresearched. The larvae are parasitic on various insects.
Families: Megaspilidae, Ceraphronidae.

Super-family: Scolioidea. These are tiny to large (40 mm) species with biting-sucking mouthparts enabling them to reach into deep flowers. The male antennae are straight, the female spiral or heart-shaped. The pterostigma is indistinct. Some are wingless. The scraping, fringer fore-legs are used for making a burrow for the night and by the females for reaching their prey (most often earth-living larvae of scarabaeid beetles).
Families: Scoliidae*, Tiphiidae, Methochidae.

Super-family: Sapygoidea. These are coloured like wasps, with which they were formerly grouped, but show no longitudinal folding of the wings. The larvae are parasitic on solitary bees.
Family: Sapygidae.

Super-family: Chrysidoidea. These are small to medium-sized species, wholly or partly metallic in colour. The antennae are 13-segmented. In the females 3—4, in the males 3—5 abdominal segments can be distinguished. The underside of the abdomen is concave. The larvae are parasitic on Tenthredinoidea, Sphecoidea, wasps, solitary bees, etc.
Families: Cleptidae, Chrysididae* (Cuckoo Wasps).

Super-family: Bethyloidea. These have an elongated body; some species are winged, some wingless. They are little known. The larvae are parasitic on various insects.
Families: Bethylidae, Dryinidae, Embolemidae.

Super-family: Mutilloidea. These are medium-sized and smaller species, often hairy and conspicuously coloured. The males are mostly winged, the females wingless. The larvae are parasitic on those of other Hymenoptera, e.g. bumblebees, digger wasps, etc.
Families: Apterogynidae, Mutillidae* (Velvet Ants), Myrmosidae.

Super-family: Formicoidea (Ants). Small or medium-sized species which are mostly yellow, brownish, browny-black or black. The antennae are angled, with up to 15 segments. The petiole between thorax and abdomen is either a knot-like single segment, or bearing a vertical scale, or two-segmented. Ants live communally. The female always founds her own nest — either by herself or by penetrating into a nest of her own or different species. The nest contains 3 castes: queens (one or more — the nest is monogynous or polygynous), workers and in certain periods winged males. The female (queen) is originally winged; after the mating flight she sheds her wings. The workers are either all identical or occur in several forms (large-headed workers are usually called soldiers). Ants are omnivorous and often cultivate aphids for their sweet secretions (honeydew). Some species are beneficial; the

species of the *Formica* genus are protected by law in some countries.
Families: Formicidae*, Dolichoderidae, Poneridae, Myrmicidae*.

Super-family: Pompiloidea. Mostly black but a part of the abdomen is red or yellow. The female digs out underground cavities for the larvae to grow in, which she provides with paralysed spiders. Species of the genus *Ceropales* lay eggs in the book lungs of spiders which have been caught by other female pompilids, while the prey is being dragged to the nest.
Families: Pompilidae, Ceropalidae.

Super-family: Vespoidea (Wasps). Medium-sized to large species, conspicuous by yellow and dark colouring. The eyes are kidney-shaped. The wings are longitudinally folded over the body. The male antennae are 13-segmented, female 12-segmented. Almost all species are solitary. Social species are the familiar paper-making wasps (*Polistes, Vespa, Vespula* and *Dolichovespula*), which create paper-like nests led by queens. Some solitary species make little clay pots stuck to plants, rocks, etc. for their offspring to develop in. Other species develop in earth banks, old wood or blackberry canes. The females provide their larvae with paralyzed caterpillars or beetle larvae. The social species are mostly predatory, the females and workers hunt flies and caterpillars as food for the larvae.
Families: Masaridae, Vespidae*.

Super-family: Sphecoidea (Digger Wasps). Medium and large species. The female antennae are 12-segmented, male mostly 13-segmented. Their colouring is variable, often yellow and black or red and black. They feed their offspring on various insect larvae or spiders which they paralyse and deposit in underground nests.
Family: Sphecidae*.

Super-family: Apoidea (Bees). Tiny, medium-sized and large species, often covered in thick hair of variable colour. The mouthparts are transformed into a sucking tube of variable length to reach the nectar at the bottom of trumpet-shaped flowers. Most species are solitary, a few are social. Social species create colonies founded by the female (queen). In solitary species the female excavates a nest and provides food for the future larvae. Some species do not build their own nest but develop in nests of solitary bees or bumblebees. Solitary bees and bumblebees are important pollinators of flowering plants. All species of bumblebees are protected by law.
Families: Colletidae*, Andrenidae*, Halictidae*, Melittidae*, Megachilidae*, Anthophoridae*, Apidae*.

Key to Identifying Some Important Groups of European Hymenoptera

1 (18) Metasoma connected to mesosoma along its whole width and length. Species always winged, wings richly veined. Fore wings with single anal cell, hind wings with more cells. Apex of front tibia with 1 or 2 spurs. Female with ovipositor of varying length . . . . Sub-order: Symphyta

2 (3) Antennae 3-segmented, last segment conspicuously long. Dark, metallic or light-coloured smaller species . . . . Family: Argidae

3 (2) Antennae with more than 3 segments

4 (5) Antennae clubbed, short. Mostly large, stout species . . . . Family: Cimbicidae

5 (4) Antennae not clubbed

6 (7) 3 normal antennal segments followed by 9 very small segments. Small species . . . . Super-family: Xyeloidea

7 (6) Antennae different from above

8 (15)	Rear margin of pronotum semi-circular	
9 (10)	Head connected to thorax by long neck. Only few species . . . . Family: Xiphydriidae	
10 (9)	Head not connected to thorax by long neck	
11 (12)	Antennae pectinate (♂) or short and serrate (♀), at least 18-segmented. On coniferous trees . . . . Family: Diprionidae	
12 (11)	Antennae not pectinate or serrate, usually 9-segmented	
13 (14)	Single spur at distal end of front tibia. Sturdy, large species, noisy fliers. Female with ovipositor of varying length . . . . Family: Siricidae	
14 (13)	2 spurs at distal end of front tibia. Antennae mostly 9-segmented. Tiny and larger species. In Europe several hundred species in many sub-families. Many difficult to identify . . . . Family: Tenthredinidae	
15 (8)	Rear margin of pronotum not semi-circular but only slightly curved	
16 (17)	Single spur on front tibia. Slender species . . . . Family: Cephidae	
17 (16)	2 spurs on front tibia. Abdomen dorsoventrally flattened. Few species . . . . Family: Pamphiliidae	
18 (1)	Metasoma not connected to mesosoma along its whole width and height but with marked con-	

stricture or waist between them. This connection can be petiolate (petiole may be 2-segmented). Mostly winged but some groups or species wingless in one sex or caste at least. Wing venation less complex, often very reduced (mainly in tiny parasitic chalcids, Proctotrupoidea, etc.). Anal cell in fore wing not developed or not enclosed. Single spur at distal end of front tibia . . . .
. . . . Sub-order: Apocrita

19 (38)   Winged species

20 (21)   Body predominantly with metal-lic sheen, surface covered in fine, richly sculptured protrusions. Underside of abdomen hollowed out, only 3—4 abdominal seg-ments visible from above. Warmth-loving, fast fliers . . . .
. . . Super-family: Chrysidoidea

21 (20)   Not predominantly metallic. If it is, more than 3—4 abdomi-nal segments visible from above and underside of abdomen is not hollowed

22 (23)   Venation of fore wing much re-duced. Mostly very tiny species, endo- or ecto-parasites of var-ious insects:
a (b) mostly metallic in colour . .
. . . Super-family: Chalcidoidea
b (a) not metallic in colour . . . .
. . Super-family: Proctotrupoidea

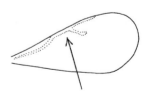

23 (22)   Venation of fore wing with at least basal veins and cross-veins.

24 (25)   A scale or nodular petiole be-tween meso- and metasoma. Antennae angled. Mostly yellow, brown or black species living so-

cially in nests (see 39 [40]) . . . .
. . . Super-family: Formicoidea

25 (24) No scale or nodular petiole between meso- and metasoma. If
petiole present, of different
shape (e.g. bell-shaped)

26 (27) Fore wing without base to costal
vein. No pterostigma, radial cell
diagonal and displaced towards
wing base. Abdomen high, with
convex sides. Tiny species,
13—16-segmented antennae.
Life-cycle complicated, in galls
on different parts of plants, often
oaks . . . .
. . . . Super-family: Cynipoidea

27 (26) Wing venation and abdomen shape different from above

28 (29) Fore wings folded longitudinally at rest. Colouring alternating yellow and black, sometimes red and black. Some species live socially in nests, ♀ and ☿ sting . . . .
. . . . Super-family: Vespoidea

29 (28) Fore wings not folded longitudinally at rest

30 (31) Antennae with more than 13 segments. Wings with rich venation.
Hindwing without basal lobe. An
areole is sometimes formed on
the front wings. Tiny and larger
species, mostly slim. Ovipositor
in females of varying length . . .
. . Super-family: Ichneumonoidea

31 (30) Antennae with no more than 13 segments. Tiny and larger
species; colouring yellow and black or red and black, many
species brownish

32 (35) Posterior tips of pronotum reaching tegulae,

33 (34) Mostly black species with red abdomen (some tiny bees also have

red abdomen but differ in other aspects). Not deeply incised between 1st and 2nd abdominal sternite. 2 spurs in the middle tibia, hind legs elongated. Female hunts and paralyses spiders . . . Super-family: Pompiloidea

34 (33) Mostly black species with yellow or whitish pattern. A deep incision between 1st and 2nd sternite. Pterostigma indistinct. Cubital and medial veins not reaching the outer edge of wing. Warmth-loving species . . . .
. . . . Family: Scoliidae

35 (32) Posterior tips of pronotum not reaching tegulae

36 (37) First segment of hind tarsi cylindrical, with cleaning spur on base. Colouring predominantly black and yellow or black and red . . . . Super-family: Sphecoidea

37 (36) First segment of hind tarsi flat, no cleaning spur; body covered with long, often vividly coloured hair (esp. *Bombinae* — bumblebees) . . . .
. . . . Super-family: Apoidea

38 (19) Wingless species*

39 (40) Vertical scale-like structure or nodular petiole between meso- and metasoma. Antenna angled, with long scape. Live communally (see 24 [25]) . . . .
. . . . Super-family: Formicoidea

40 (39) Meso- and metasoma not joined by scale or nodular petiole. Antennae not angled

41 (42) Abdomen higher than its width, with convex sides. Individuals only several mm long, can be reared from galls (see 26 [27]) . . . .
. . . . Super-family: Cynipoidea

42 (41)   Abdomen wider than its height, without convex sides. Body
           sometimes covered with thick hair. Individuals with sting . .
           . . . . Family: Mutillidae — ♀ ; (males winged)

---

*) The key does not include wingless species of super-families Ichneu-
monoidea, Chalcidoidea, Proctotrupoidea and Bethyloidea, whose
identification requires good optical equipment and specialized literature.

Plates

Family: Pamphillidae — Web-spinning and Leaf-rolling Sawflies

⊗ *Acantholyda erythrocephala* (L.) shows marked differences between the sexes. The female **(2)** has a reddish-brown head with a blue spot between the ocelli, while the male **(1)** has a blue head. It lives mostly in young (10—15-year-old) pine woods where the adults are on the wing in late April and May. It develops on various species of pine. The female lays her eggs on the previous year's needles. The larva is shiny, greenish-grey, with longitudinal stripes and brown spots. The larvae feed on pine needles and make a communal refuge of loosely spun silk on young branches. The refuge is smooth on the surface. The full-grown larva is about 20 mm long. In mid-June it leaves the tree, burrows into the ground and pupates. The life cycle lasts 1—3 years. Sometimes claimed to be harmful to young pines.

It is widespread in Europe, introduced in USA.
Length 10—12 mm, wingspan 20—26 mm.

⊙ *Cephalcia abietis* (L.) The sexes are markedly different in both shape and colour. The abdomen of the female is mostly yellow, while that of the male has black transverse bands dorsally. In males the sides of the abdomen are almost parallel, while in the females they are rounded **(3,4)**. It inhabits the older stands of spruce in the foothills and mountain regions where it can be very numerous in some years. The adults fly slowly and are on the wing from mid-April till the end of June. The female lays about 100—120 eggs in batches of 4—10 in an incision made with her ovipositor in a previous year's needle. The larvae live communally in brownish, silken sacs which they spin on branches of the host tree. Protected by the sac, they feed on the older needles from the top of the tree downwards. The sac fills with excreta, needle debris and cast-off larval skins. Affected trees are conspicuous due to the attached groups of sacs. The full-grown larva is about 20—25 mm long, mostly deep green, sometimes brownish. At the end of summer it falls to the ground and burrows 5—25 cm deep; there it makes a chamber where it rests for up to 3 years before pupating. The larva about to pupate can be distinguished by the sharply outlined pupal eyes. Adults, larvae and pupae have many enemies amongst insects and birds, as well as mammals.

Widespread over most of temperate part of Eurasia.
Length ♂ 11 mm, ♀ 14 mm; wingspan ♂ 20—24 mm, ♀ 22—27 mm.

⊙ *Neurotoma nemoralis* (L.) often lives in gardens. The female **(5)** prefers cherry, plum, apricot, peach, sloe and other similar fruit trees. She lays about 60—70 eggs on the underside of the young leaves of the host plant. The larvae feed on the leaf tissue. Prior to moulting their first skin they live communally, then they disperse and hide in rolled-up leaves. Later they spin together the affected leaves and so create large nests which are gradually filled with excreta. The larvae are very voracious and can defoliate whole trees. The full-grown larva either descends on a thread it has produced or crawls down the tree to the ground, where it burrows down and spins a cocoon in which it pupates in the spring. The imagines appear in late April to May. There is a single generation per year. Sometimes harmful.

N. nemoralis is widespread throughout Europe.
Length 8—10 mm, wingspan 15—17 mm.

1 ♂

2 ♀

3 ♀

4 ♀

5 ♀

Family: Siricidae — Horntails or Wood Wasps

⊗ **Sirex juvencus** (L.) exhibits not only sexual dimorphism (the female ovipositor is much shorter than the abdomen — **1,2**) but also sexual dichroism (different colouring). Most segments of the male **(3)** abdomen are red-yellow, while the female abdomen is a shiny purple-black. *S. juvencus* typically inhabits coniferous (mostly pine) woodland where the adults fly in the clearings on sunny days between June and August and even into September. The female lays eggs in trees damaged by bark-beetle, fungi, wind or fire or in dead wood. The relatively short ovipositor makes inserting eggs deep into the wood difficult, therefore the female deposits the eggs in young trees, or — in older trees — into branches with thin bark. It prefers pine but also utilizes spruce and fir. The number of eggs is variable (350—480) but they are always laid in pairs. The individual eggs are covered by a mucous layer containing spores of wood-attacking fungi; these are kept in special sacs in the female's body. The spores are inserted into the wood along with the eggs, develop into mycelia which spread through tunnels made by the larvae and serve as their food. The tunnels are narrow at first but wider as the larvae grow; they are 15—25 centimetres long and blocked by chewed-up debris. After tunnelling inside the trunk, the larva returns to just below the surface of the wood where it makes a pupal chamber and pupates. Development takes 2—3 years.

S. juvencus is sometimes recorded as a timber pest. Like *Urocerus gigas* (L.) and similar species, it is sometimes found in urban situations, when it has emerged from roof beams.

It is distributed throughout a large part of Europe, North Africa and temperate Asia; it has been introduced into Australia.
Length ♂ 12—28 mm, ♀ 15—30 mm.

Xeris spectrum (L.) A mostly black species with yellow spots on the sides of the prothorax **(5)**. The legs are partly red-yellow. The long cylindrical body of the female **(4)** carries an ovipositor approximately equalling the body length. The ovipositor may give the impression of a dangerous weapon but the female is quite harmless to man; the ovipositor serves only for egg-laying.

X. spectrum inhabits coniferous, mostly pine, woods. The adults fly on warm sunny days and are also found in country houses. The female lays her eggs mainly in pine wood but also spruce, fir and possibly oak. She deposits them in cracks caused by the drying-out of wood. The larva feeds on cellulose as the female, unlike other related species, has no sacs for the spores of wood-attacking fungi. The larvae overwinter in the wood. Development takes 2—3 years. Larvae and pupae are introduced into towns in timber; thus from time to time adults are found in urban situations.

X. spectrum is distributed over most of Europe, Siberia, China and Japan.
Length 15—30 mm.

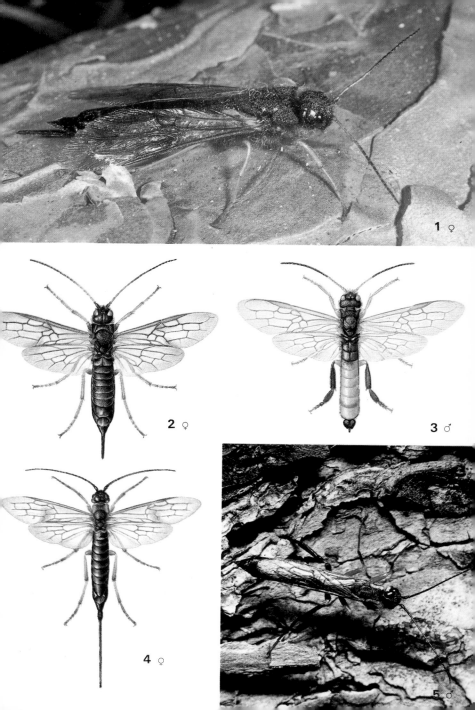

1 ♀

2 ♀

3 ♂

4 ♀

5 ♂

Family: Siricidae — Horntails or Wood Wasps

⊗ *Urocerus gigas* (L.) — Greater Horntail — is one of the largest European Hymenoptera. The cylindrical body of the female has a relatively long and thick ovipositor (1) which has a complicated structure. *U. gigas* shows both sexual
dimorphism and sexual dichroism (difference in colour between the sexes), especially in the abdomen. Similar in size to two other species, it can be distinguished by its predominantly black head. In *U. augur* the head is all yellow and in
U. phantoma yellow with a black groove.

U. gigas is a forest species, preferring light and sunny places with fallen tree-
trunks. It frequently occurs in country houses where it is introduced in timber.
A fast and noisy flier, it is on the wing on sunny days in summer, sometimes as
early as May. The 'wasp-like' coloration of the female — a combination of black
and yellow — makes people cautious and they give a sitting or flying *Urocerus*
a wide berth. It is, however, not at all dangerous because it does not sting.

For egg-laying the females seek out either freshly felled trees with bark still
intact or living trees which are diseased. The female inserts her ovipositor vertically into the wood about 5—10 mm deep; considering the hardness
of the wood and the fragility of insect bodies, it is a remarkable achievement.
She lays 4—8 eggs at a time. The overall number of eggs laid varies greatly
(50—350). The larvae hatch out in about 4 weeks. First they remain near the surface of the wood, later they penetrate deep into it but finally they return to just
below the surface where they pupate in a chamber. The larva's return to the surface makes it easier for the emerging adult to bite its way out. The feeding larva
leaves a tunnel up to 400 mm long, firmly packed with chewed-up debris. The
full-grown larva is fat, cylindrical and whitish in colour. It is blind and has three
pairs of thoracic legs and a short, sharp brown spike at the posterior end of its
body. The pupa is not enclosed in a cocoon. It is yellowish-white and shows
clearly the body appendages of the future imago. Development takes 2—3
years. The hatched adult bites its way out of the wood through a circular hole.
Circular exit holes in tree-trunks betray the presence of *U. gigas* in a locality. It
can be plentiful in some years but even then the harm it does is negligible.

U. gigas is distributed over a large part of Europe, temperate Asia and North
Africa.
Length ♂ 12—32 mm, ♀ 24—44 mm.

Family: Xiphydriidae

⊗ *Xiphydria camelus* (L.) is the most common member of this small family. Like
other Xiphydriidae, it has a conspicuously long neck. It is easily differentiated
from the other species in the family by the white stripes on its head; these
stripes do not reach the eyes (2,3). The larvae usually develop in alder trees but
in some localities they occur in birches.

X. camelus is widespread throughout Eurasia.
Length 10—21 mm.

1 ♀

2

3

Family Argidae

⊗ **Arge ochropus** (GMEL. IN L.), often given the scientific name of *A. rosae,* is one of several species of sawflies feeding on and injurious to rose bushes. It resembles *A. pagana* which, however, has dark legs. In *A. ochropus* the femur and tibia are almost yellow. The adults **(1,2)** are often found on Umbelliferae. The 3-segmented antennae have a small first and second segment and an elongated third segment.

There are usually two generations a year. The adults of the first generation appear in May, the second generation flies in July and August. The larvae develop on dog rose and some varieties of cultivated rose. The female of the first generation lays her eggs in young shoots in May. The batches of about 16—18 eggs are laid in incisions in the epidermis of the host plant and resemble an elongated chain. The newly hatched larvae feed on the upper epidermis of the leaves, never destroying the lower cell layers. In the next instar they feed from the edge of the leaf and devour the whole tissue. They adopt a characteristic pose on the leaves: the abdomen is either held erect in the shape of an S, or coiled and hanging under the leaf. The full-grown larva is stout, about 20 mm long, with 9 pairs of extremities. Prior to pupation it falls from the host plant and pupates in a cocoon in the ground.

A. ochropus is widespread throughout Europe, Siberia and Asia Minor.
Length 7—10 mm.

⊗ **Arge nigripes** (RETZ.) resembles several other dark-coloured species. The main difference is in the venation of the fore wing. The larvae live on Rosaceae and the adults **(3)** frequent various herbaceous and woody plants.

A. nigripes is widespread throughout Europe.
Length 7—9 mm.

Family: Cimbicidae

⊗ **Cimbex femorata** (L.) — Birch Sawfly — is usually black **(4,5)**. There is some variation in colour of individuals; some have yellowish spots on the abdomen, whereas in some others this part of the body is completely dark red. There is a brownish line along the front edge of the fore wings. The adults fly awkwardly in birch woods in May and June. The female lays her eggs singly in the tissue of birch leaves. She makes a slit in the leaf with her ovipositor, thus creating a small pocket to protect the egg. The caterpillar-like larva has 11 pairs of extremities, is slow-moving, light green with a dark dorsal stripe and dark spots round the breathing holes or spiracles. The larvae feed at night on birch leaves, resting on the underside during the day. When in danger, they can spray haemolymph as far as 200 mm and thus deter potential attackers. In September the caterpillar-like larva is fully grown (up to 45 mm long). It spins — often on a branch — an elongated dark-brown cocoon, in which it overwinters and then pupates in the spring. There is a single generation each year. They do not cause a great deal of harm, even in large numbers. This species is a conspicuous and decorative inhabitant of birch woods.

C. femorata is widespread throughout Europe and Siberia.
Length 20—28 mm.

Family: Diprionidae

⊗ **Diprion pini** (L.) — Pine Sawfly — exhibits both sexual dichroism and dimorphism. The female **(1,3)** antennae have 19—20 segments and taper towards the tips. The male **(2,4)** antennae have 20—21 segments and are strongly pectinate.
D. pini lives in pinewoods, prefering younger, diseased stands on poor soil. There can be one or two generations a year. When there is only a single generation, the adults fly in June and July, in the case of two generations in April/May and then again in July/August. The female lays about 100—150 eggs in pine needles. First she makes an incision in the needle with her ovipositor, then deposits in it up to 20 eggs and covers them with a protective layer. In spring, the previous year's needles are used, while in summer newly grown ones are also used. The larvae live gregariously on the needles **(5)**. When there are two generations, they are found in May/June and later from August to October. First they feed on the sides of the needles, sparing the main vein and the tip (first generation larvae do not eat the current year's needles). Later they feed on whole needles and some times also the bark of young shoots. They can completely defoliate a tree. The larva is pale yellow to yellowish-green, with a small brown head and 11 pairs of extremities. Fully grown it can be up to 26 mm long; then it ceases to feed and looks for a suitable place to pupate in. The larvae of the first generation usually crawl into cracks in the bark, although some stay on the needles and branches. They spin brown, barrel-shaped, hard cocoons in which they pupate. The pupae form in July and the imagines emerge in the same month. The larvae of the second generation, which are fully grown in the autumn, burrow into the soil at the base of the tree and overwinter there in cocoons. The adult bites out a lid from the cocoon, which allows it to emerge.

Pine sawflies have many enemies among other insects and higher animals. They are hunted by Ichneumonidae (more than 30 species), predatory beetles and numerous birds (woodpeckers, tits, cuckoos, etc.).

D. pini is distributed over a large part of Eurasia and North Africa.
Length ♂ 7—8 mm, ♀ 7.5—10 mm.

⊗ **Neodiprion sertifer** (GEOFFR.) develops on pine trees. The adults appear in the second half of August and the beginning of September. The female **(6)** lays her eggs in the needles of Scots, Swiss Mountain and Austrian Pine. The eggs overwinter and the larvae hatch out between April and June, depending on the altitude. They feed on the needles and pupate in July. It is sometimes harmful.

N. sertifer inhabits a large part of Europe.
Length ♂ 6—8 mm, ♀ 7—9 mm.

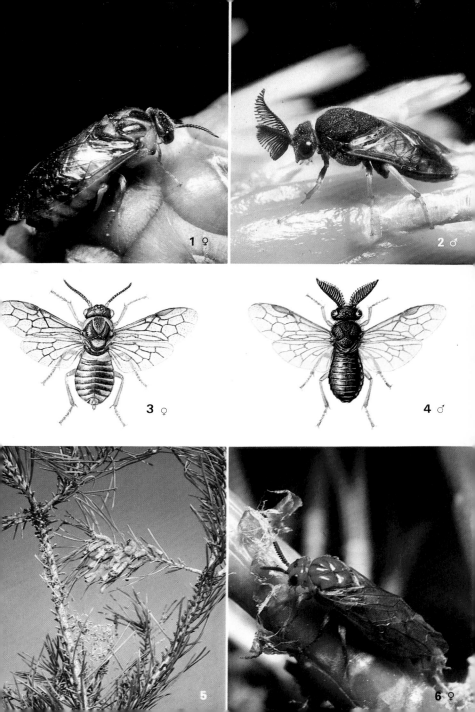

1 ♀

2 ♂

3 ♀

4 ♂

5

6 ♀

Family: Tenthredinidae — Typical Sawflies

⊗ *Macrophya montana* (Scop.), in older literature known as *M. rustica,* is distinguished along with a number of similar species by the length of the hind femur. The hind femur and tibia are approximately the same length **(1)**. This very common sawfly frequents flowering Umbelliferae.
It is widespread throughout Europe, Asia Minor and North Africa.
Length ♂ 10 mm, ♀ 10—12 mm.

⊙ *Tenthredo campestris* L. (formerly *T. flavicornis*) passes its larval stages on ground elder (*Aegopodium podagraria*). The abdomen of this sawfly is partly red **(2)**, as is the pronotum, while the mesonotum is reddish in most cases but black in some individuals (form called *luteicornis*).
The adults are common between May and August and frequent various flowering plants. The length of the larvae is up to 20 mm. When full-grown, they burrow in the earth where they spin a cocoon and later pupate.
This sawfly inhabits most of Europe.
Length 13—14 mm.

⊗ *Rhogogaster viridis* (L.) resembles *R. picta* and *R. punctulata* in general appearance and colouring. They are all coloured vivid green which either predominates or may be almost suppressed by black. In individuals preserved in collections this bright green changes to yellow. The above species can be distinguished by the following features: *R. viridis* **(3,4)** is green with a dark dorsal stripe down the centre of the abdomen and no dark spots along the sides. *R. punctulata* has double dark spots along the sides. *R. picta* is predominantly black with light green markings.
R. viridis is very common and conspicuous. The adults fly in summer and hunt various insect species, among which Colorado Beetle larvae have been noted. The larvae are herbivorous and feed on the leaves of various trees (willow, poplar, alder, etc.) and herbaceous plants (buttercups, etc.).
R. viridis is widespread through a greater part of the Palaearctic region (Europe, temperate Asia as far as Japan) and North America.
Length 10—13 mm.

⊗ *Tenthredo zonula* Klug. is 'wasp-coloured', with alternating bands of black and yellow. It can be easily distinguished from wasps by its wide first abdominal segment which is attached to the thorax across its whole width **(5)**. It also lacks a sting but checking this may be too risky to count as a distinguishing feature. The wasp colouring shows also on the legs; the hind femur is almost yellow, with a little black at the top. The adults **(6)** are common in summer, especially on flowering Umbelliferae, alongside other Tenthredinidae, wasps, ichneumons and other Hymenoptera. The larvae develop on St John's Wort (Hypericum).
T. zonula is widespread in Europe, Asia Minor and North Africa.
Length 9—10 mm.

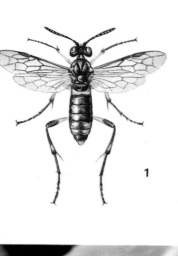

Family: Tenthredinidae — Typical Sawflies

⊗ **Allantus cinctus** (L.). The males differ from the females in colour; the male abdomen is either all dark or bears a white spot on the first abdominal tergite while in the females **(1)** this spot is more pronounced and the 5th tergite is all white. The wings are yellowish with brownish-red veins in both sexes. The adults are associated with rose bushes but are not the only Tenthredinidae whose development is connected with roses.

There are two generations a year. The female lays her eggs on the underside of the leaves of rose (sometimes strawberry). The larvae are predominantly dark green to blue-green with a yellowish-brown head. They feed on the leaf tissues; they rest coiled on the leaves but fall to the ground when disturbed. The full-grown larva is about 10—15 mm long. Before pupating it enters a twig or broken shoot, in which it bores a tunnel some 20 mm long and closes the opening with pulp. It also pupates in crevices in walls, fences, etc. This species is not a pest.

It is found in a large part of Europe and Siberia and has been introduced into North America.
Length 7—10 mm.

⊗ **Athalia rosae** (L.). also known as *A. colibri,* is mostly red and yellow and has two and more generations a year. The first generation flies in May, the second in July, the third in August and September; sometimes there is a fourth generation in October. The adults **(2,3)** frequent the flowerheads of Compositae, Umbelliferae and Cruciferae to take the pollen and nectar. They are slow and easy to catch.

The female lays up to 300 eggs in the leaves of cultivated and wild Cruciferae. She sits astride the leaf edge and separates the upper and lower layers of the leaf with her finely serrated ovipositor; there she deposits a single egg. The egg is kidney-shaped, whitish-yellow and less than 1 mm long. On hatching, the larva bores a tunnel in the leaf and then emerges to eat out holes in the lower surface of the leaves. Later it moves to the upper surface of the leaves and the leaf edges. The full-grown larva then burrows into the soil, makes a cocoon of soil particles lined with silk and pupates. The female cocoon is larger than that of the male.

In dry and warm summers the larvae can be injurious to various cultivated Cruciferae, especially oil-seed rape, mustard, cabbage, etc. Occasionally they can completely strip the plants. The worst damage is caused by the second generation. The larvae have many enemies among nematodes and insects (mainly ichneumons and chalcids).

A. rosae occurs over the greater part of Eurasia, North and southern Africa and South America.
Length 6—8 mm.

1 ♀

2

3

Family: Tenthredinidae — Typical Sawflies

⊗ **Phymatocera aterrima** (KLUG) is black all over, as its name suggests (*ater* — black). The antennae of the female are the same length as the abdomen, while in the male they are longer and covered in fine bristles.

This sawfly lives in deciduous forests where the larvae develop on various species of Solomon's Seal and Lily-of-the-Valley. Sometimes it is a garden pest. The adults fly in the spring and are relatively slow and easy to catch.

The female (3) lays her eggs (2) in the stem of Solomon's seal and appears to prefer the straight stems of *Polygonatum verticillatum*. She pierces the epidermis with her ovipositor, hollows out a small chamber and deposits a single egg in it, thus protecting the egg from adverse weather and predatory insects. Several eggs are laid in a line. Initially the larva feeds on the surrounding tissue, then bores its way out of the stem and moves to the leaves which are its main food. The young larvae feed communally. Most of them stay on the underside of the leaves where they sit tightly packed together with their heads all facing the same way (1). They start feeding on the underside of the leaves and then make holes and enlarge them. The young larvae do not chew through the parallel leaf veins but make holes between them. Older larvae eat the veins as well and the leaf blade gradually disappears, with the exception of the main vein. The larvae are very typical, long and relatively slim, greyish with a dark head. The head is light-coloured after moulting but after a few hours darkens again. The full-grown larvae burrow into the soil to pupate in cocoons.

P. aterrima is widespread especially in central and southern Europe.
Length 8—9 mm.

⊗ **Blennocampa pusilla** (KLUG) is predominantly black with white distal ends to the femora and white tibiae and tarsi; the distal ends of the hind tibiae and tarsi are brown. It is a tiny, rather inconspicuous but common species. The adults (4) fly in May and June. The larvae develop on rose bushes.

The female lays her eggs singly or in twos or threes on the underside of the edges of rose leaves. The newly hatched larva is white but later turns green with a brown head and black eyes and antennae. The young larvae roll the edges of a rose leaf to form two tubes parallel to the main vein (5). These tubes are inhabited by one or two larvae which feed on the leaf tissue. In July the larvae grow to about 8—9 mm, leave their tubes and burrow into the ground. There they make cocoons in which they overwinter and pupate in the spring. They are disliked by rose-growers for disfiguring the leaves.

B. pusilla is widespread over a large part of the Palaearctic region.
Length 4 mm.

1

2 ♀

3 ♀

4

5

Family: Tenthredinidae — Typical Sawflies

⊗ *Hoplocampa flava* (L.) inhabits gardens. The adults **(1)** emerge from the soil as early as April and are still on the wing in May. They spend most of their lives in the tops of trees and are hence less often seen than the larvae. The adults seem to prefer feeding on the nectar and pollen of plum blossom, where they are often found in large numbers in the early morning.

The fertilized female lays about 70 eggs. She seeks out flowers that are just opening, inserts one egg into the calyx tissue of each and seals the cut with a special secretion. The tiny larva makes its way quickly to the ovary and feeds on its surface. Later it penetrates inside and devours the developing fruit, leaving dark-coloured excreta in the tunnel. It destroys several young fruits before it is fully grown, by which time it is pale yellow. It then falls to the ground within an infested fruit, leaves it and burrows about 15 cm deep. There it spins a cocoon and overwinters before pupating in the spring. The larva causes premature fruit fall but the damage is not significant; on the contrary, in a good season it can have a positive influence as it contributes towards a 'selection' process. It is incorrectly accused of causing 'worms' in plums.

H. flava is widespread throughout most of Europe.
Length 4—5 mm.

⊗ *Caliroa cerasi* (L.) — Pearl Sawfly or Slugworm — often described as *C. limacina*, is a unicolour sawly **(2)** living in woods and gardens. There are two generations a year; the spring adults leave the soil at the beginning of May.

The female lays her eggs singly in the leaves of various trees and bushes, mainly cherry, pear, rowan, hawthorn, birch and rose. She makes an incision with her ovipositor to create a tiny chamber where she deposits the egg. The newly hatched larvae feed on the upper surface of the leaf, gradually reducing it to a skeleton but without disturbing the veins. At first the caterpillar-like larva is unlike other sawfly larvae — it is black with a club-like, broadened front part and covered in slime with an inky smell **(3)**. It resembles a slug, from which its old scientific name is derived (*limax* — slug). In the last larval stage it no longer exudes slime. When grown to about 10 mm, it falls to the ground and makes a shallow burrow. There it spins an egg-shaped cocoon in which it pupates. The adults emerge after about two weeks and form the second or August generation. The larvae of this generation feed during September and October and sometimes are so numerous as to strip entire plants of their leaves. These larvae overwinter and pupate in the spring. Large numbers of larvae are detrimental to the whole plant as the attacked leaves turn yellow and fall off, leading to premature fruit fall. The weakened host plant is subsequently less fertile.

C. cerasi occurs almost all over the world and has been introduced into North America and Australia.
Length about 5 mm, wingspan 10 mm.

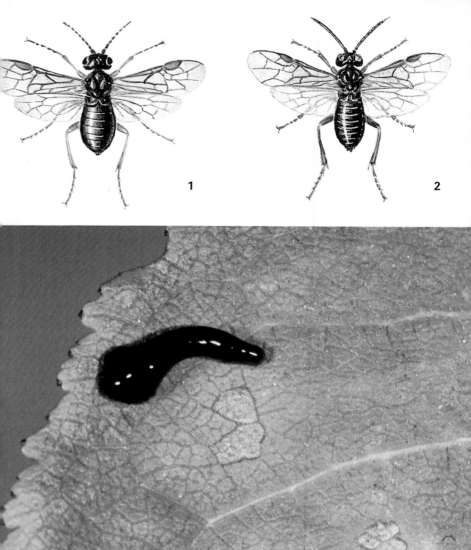

1

2

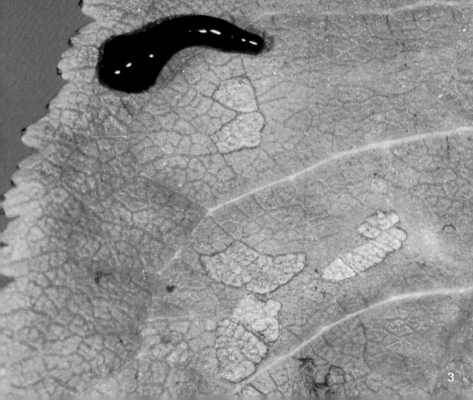

3

Family: Tenthredinidae — Typical Sawflies

⊗ **Croesus septentrionalis** (L.) This sawfly **(1)**, whose abdomen is predominantly red, flies in May. The larvae are more interestingly coloured than the adults — they are very striking, green with black spots and a black head. The last two or three body segments are yellowish with black spots.

The larvae occur on the leaves of birch and alder but are also found on other deciduous trees. They feed on the leaf margins and when disturbed adopt a threatening posture, all simultaneously rearing up and curving their bodies into a question-mark shape. They either remain immobile in this strange position for some time or move the upright part. They pupate in the soil.

C. septentrionalis occurs over the whole of Europe.
Length 7—10 mm.

⊗ **Trichiocampus viminalis** (FALL.) — Poplar Sawfly **(2)** — flies in May and is common in avenues of poplar trees. The male antennae are covered with long hair and have a short, blunt protrusion on the third segment. The caterpillar-like larva has a greenish body, yellowish at each end, and a black head. The whole body is covered in black spots. The larvae feed on the leaves of sallow and various species of poplar.

The female lays her eggs in two parallel rows in the petiole of the leaf. The larvae live gregariously, like in many other sawflies, and feed together on the undersides of leaves; they can strip whole trees bare and have an unpleasant odour. The larvae occur up until the autumn. At about 20 mm in length, they crawl into crevices in the bark and pupate in cocoons.

T. viminalis is widespread throughout central and northern Europe.
Length about 9 mm.

⊗ **Nematus ribesii** (SCOP.) — Gooseberry Sawfly — develops on the leaves of gooseberry, blackcurrant, redcurrant and white currant. The males and females differ in colour — the female **(3)** abdomen is yellow, the male abdomen black above and yellow beneath.

There are 2 to 4 generations a year. The first generation of adults appears in April. The female lays about 50 eggs into the main veins on the underside of the leaves of the host plants. She makes an incision with her ovipositor and lays a row of eggs in this groove in such a way that they partly protrude. The larvae hatch in 7—15 days and feed on leaf tissue. At first they remain inside the bush and gradually move on towards the perimeter. In large numbers they can defoliate whole plants, leaving only the stems and strong veins. The full-grown larva burrows into the soil and spins a reddish-brown parchment-like cocoon, in which it pupates. The length of the life-cycle depends on the season — the autumn larvae overwinter in their cocoons and pupate in the spring.

N. ribesii occurs mainly in central and northern Europe; it was introduced into North America in mid-19th century.
Length 6—8 mm, span of fore wings 14—16 mm.

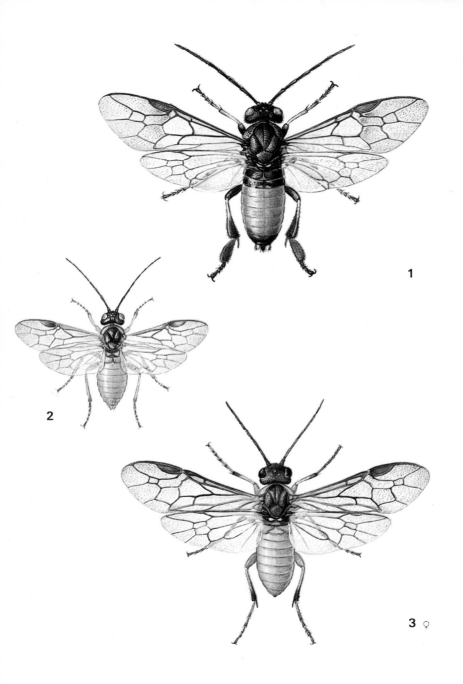

1

2

3 ♀

Family: Ichneumonidae — Ichneumon Flies

⊗ *Rhyssa persuasoria* (L.) is the most common of several large, similar long-legged species. The dark body has white spots on the thorax and abdominal segments but does not have white rings on the antennae. This species frequents coniferous woods, especially paths and clearings with felled trees.

The female is equipped with a very long, needle-thin ovipositor **(1)**. She also has very sensitive sense-organs (e.g. on the antennae and the legs), which help her to locate her prey — the large larvae of Siricidae (horntail wasps) — *Urocerus gigas, Sirex juvencus* and *Xeris spectrum,* etc., and sometimes those of several large longicorn beetles. The larvae tunnel into the wood of felled trees and are sometimes several centimetres deep. The searching female flies around and when she senses her prey, she settles on the log. She inserts her ovipositor into the wood and after penetrating as far as the body of the larva she lays her egg. The whole process can take from 20 to 40 minutes but even that is a very short time. It is no simple matter for this female; she has to expend a great deal of ingenuity and energy to drill through the thick, hard wood. The female's drilling stance is characteristic: the abdomen is turned upwards and pressure applied to drive the ovipositor into the wood **(2)**. However, she does not rotate the ovipositor as some ichneumons do. After laying, the ovipositor is withdrawn from the wood and the female flies off to search for another larva. Sometimes her efforts are in vain as she cannot penetrate deep enough to reach the larva. During oviposition the female is very vulnerable because she cannot withdraw the ovipositor quickly and fly away. *R. persuasoria* larvae feed on the body tissues of horntail wasp larvae. They overwinter and pupate in the spring. There is a single generation each year.

R. persuasoria occurs over a large part of the Palaearctic and Nearctic region. Length ♂ 18—40 mm, ♀ with ovipositor up to 80 mm.

⊙ *Megarhyssa superba* (Schr.) belongs to the largest of the European ichneumons. The body is rust-coloured with yellow patterning on the thorax and yellow spots on the sides of the abdomen **(3)**.

This species inhabits deciduous forests where the female seeks out the larvae of large horntail wasps, especially *Xiphydria camelus* and *Tremex fuscicornis.* Their body tissues provide the food for the ichneumon larvae. As the host species are less common, this beautiful ichneumon tends to be scarce.

M. superba occurs over a large part of Eurasia. Length of body ♂ 19—34 mm, ♀ with ovipositor up to 90 mm.

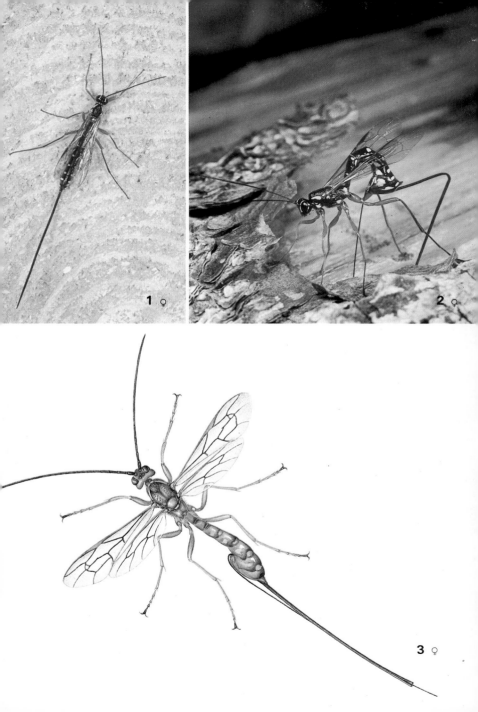

1 ♀

2 ♀

3 ♀

Family: Ichneumonidae — Ichneumon Flies

⊗ **Pimpla instigator** (F.) is a fairly common inhabitant of woods. The size of its body is influenced by the quantity of food available during the larval stage. The black-coloured adult is covered on the head and propodeum with black hair; in the very similar *P. examinator* this hair is light-coloured. The imago of *P. instigator* resembles other species, above all *P. illecebrator*. *P. instigator* has red hind tibiae, *P. illecebrator* black ones. The female (1, 2) has a relatively short ovipositor, approximately the length of the hind tibia. As in many other ichneumon species, the imagines smell of asphalt.

The female either flies or runs on the ground with her wings slightly raised while searching for lepidopteran pupae — the food for her future larvae. From this point of view she is not very selective. Her main concern is not finding a particular species but making sure the pupa is the correct size. She uses the pupae of many species of Lepidoptera, e.g. *Malacosoma neustrium* and the Gipsy Moth (*Lymantria dispar*), but also the quite unrelated Large White butterfly (*Pieris brassicae*). Among her hosts are also some Hymenoptera, e.g. the Birch Sawfly (*Cimbex femorata*). The *P. instigator* female penetrates her prey with her ovipositor and inserts an egg. The eggs can only be laid in temperatures above 20 °C.

The imagines seem to feed mainly on flower nectar but are not averse to animal food. The female has the opportunity to suck haemolymph from the pupae she penetrates. The male will make use of a parasitized pupa but cannot perforate it himself.

The adult overwinters under the dead bark of standing and felled trees; large numbers may occasionally be found in such places. Like most other ichneumons, *P. instigator* is important in controlling pests.

It is widespread throughout the Palaearctic region.
Length 10—24 mm.

⊗ **Metopius pinatorius** BRUL. is the most common species of the genus. This ichneumon, previously known as *M. micratorius,* resembles a wasp in its yellow and black coloration (3).

The female lays her eggs into the caterpillars of many Lepidoptera species. The larva lives in the host's body as an endoparasite. Among the hosts are not only several common moths (e.g. *Acronicta psi*) but also some pests like *Malacosoma neustrium* or rare species like *Saturnia pyri*, etc.

This species ranges from western Europe to eastern Siberia and the Caucasus.
Length 14—17 mm.

 1 ♀

 2 ♀

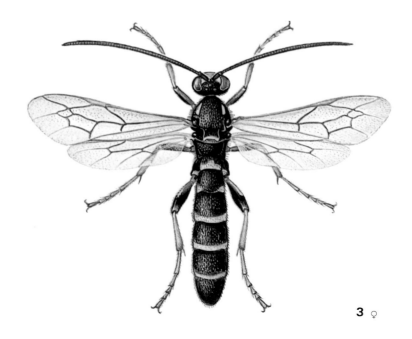 3 ♀

Family: Ichneumonidae — Ichneumon Flies

⊗ *Enicospilus ramidulus* (L.) is one of the many species of the sub-family Ophioninae. They are all relatively large and very similar in appearance, being rust-coloured with a laterally compressed abdomen. These ichneumons are difficult to identify. Until recently all rust-coloured ichneumons seen in the evening light were referred to as the Yellow Ichneumon (*Ophion luteus*). The detailed study of material in collections has demonstrated that there is a complex of species with different distributions. Strangely, the Yellow Ichneumon was found to be relatively rare.

Species belonging to the genera *Enicospilus* and *Ophion* have no distinct thickened area, the areolus, on their fore wings which is common in other ichneumons. Species of the genus *Enicospilus* can be distinguished from similar ichneumons by one to three sclerotized rust-coloured spots of varying sizes on their fore-wings. The adults of *E. ramidulus* (1) have two such spots; they are easily visible under a magnifying glass. The female has only a short ovipositor. The larvae feed mainly on the caterpillars of the Pine Beauty Moth (*Panolis flammea*), into which the female inserts her eggs.

E. ramidulus is widespread in the central and southern parts of the Palaearctic region.
Length 18—20 mm.

⊗ *Therion circumflexum* (L.), in older literature referred to as *Exochilum circumflexum*, is a relatively common species in pine woods. The adults (2) fly in late spring and have a characteristic posture when in flight. The antennae are pointed upwards, the hind legs are spread wide apart and the abdomen arched downwards. These ichneumons are partial to the sweet excreta of aphids.

The female inserts her eggs into the caterpillars of some species of Lepidoptera. Because the larvae are rather large, she searches out the caterpillars of the larger lepidopterans, e.g. Sphingidae (especially the Privet Hawk Moth — *Sphinx ligustri* and the Pine Hawk Moth — *Hyloicus pinastri*), some species of Notodontidae, Lasiocampidae and various Noctuidae. The full-grown parasite larva pupates in a scanty cocoon. The accumulated excreta of the larva create a protective cup-shaped layer which fills most of the cocoon; this holds the back part of the pupa. The cast-off larval skin lies at the bottom of this cup.

This species is distributed over a large part of the Palaearctic and Nearctic regions.
Length 15—25 mm; length of fore wing 7—16 mm.

⊗ *Ichneumon stramentarius* Grav. is a common species. The antennae are usually 37—40-segmented. In the autumn the females (3) crawl under the bark of fallen trees and tree-stumps, where they often hibernate communally. Their development is similar to that of other ichneumons.

I. stramentarius is distributed over most of Europe.
Length 11—14 mm.

1

2

3 ♀

Family: Ichneumonidae — Ichneumon Flies

⊗ *Ichneumon sarcitorius* L. is a conspicuous species, described more than two hundred years ago by the Swedish naturalist C. Linnaeus. It belongs to a genus which now contains many species. The males and females of this species show marked differences in colour. The male (1) shows the typical 'wasp' coloration, while in the female red and white are added. The coloration is very variable in both sexes. Dichroism is also apparent in the antennae; in males their upper side is black, while in the females they are partly brown, white and black.

The adults frequent flowering umbels of ground elder, hogweed, carrrot, wild angelica, etc. but are also attracted to the flowers of the spurge family. The females overwinter. In the egg-laying season the female searches out the caterpillars of various Lepidoptera, in which she lays her eggs. The most common host appears to be the Turnip Moth (*Agrotis segetum*) but larvae have been found on the Gipsy Moth (*Lymantria dispar*), the White Ermine (*Spilosoma menthastri*), etc.

This species is distributed over a large part of the Palaearctic region. Length 10—15 mm.

⊗ *Amblyteles armatorius* (FÖRST.) is at present the only member of this genus. Until recently the genus *Amblyteles* included many dozens of related and similar species which have since been transferred to other genera. All exhibited the typical 'wasp' coloration of yellow and dark colours alternating. *A. armatorius* shows sexual dichroism, most noticeable in the colour of the abdomen and the legs. The females (3) have rust-coloured tibiae and tarsi, while in the males the tibiae are yellow (2).

The adults are common on flowering plants. The female overwinters and then parasitizes the caterpillars of various moths. This species is distributed over the greater part of the Palaearctic region. Length 12—16 mm.

⊗ *Protichneumon pisorius* (L.) inhabits spruce forests. The two sexes are markedly different. The female has white orbits on her head and a white ring on her hind tibia. In the male (4) both the cheeks and the base of the propodeum are white.

The sturdy adults are fond of sitting on flowering Umbelliferae in forest clearings. The females specifically parasitize the caterpillars of various hawk moths, whose size guarantees a sufficient supply of food for the future larvae. Their main hosts are the caterpillars of the Pine Hawk Moth (*Hyloicus pinastri*), the Privet Hawk Moth (*Sphinx ligustri*), the Poplar Hawk Moth (*Laothoe populi*) and the Eyed Hawk Moth (*Smerinthus ocellatus*). The female ichneumon inserts her ovipositor into the caterpillar and introduces a single egg. The ichneumon larva then develops in the caterpillar's body. It feeds slowly on the caterpillar's body tissue but does not kill it. The full-grown caterpillar spins a cocoon and moults into a pupa but out of the pupa emerges not a moth but an adult ichneumon.

P. pisorius is common throughout a large part of the Palaearctic region. Length 22—28 mm.

1 ♂

2 ♂

3 ♀

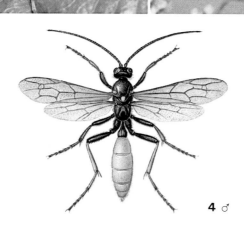

4 ♂

Family: Braconidae

⊗ **Spathius exarator** (L.) is one of the largest braconid wasps in this very varied and extensive family. In spite of this it is not very conspicuous in either size or colour. It can be distinguished from related species by the length of the abdominal petiole which is equal in length to all the following segments put together. The female (**1, 3**) differs from the male (**2**) in possessing an ovipositor which is the same length as her body.

This species is a common and regular visitor to houses where there is woodworm (esp. *Anobium punctatum*) living in the old wood (furniture, beams, floorboards). If we find woodworm in the house, it is very likely that we will find *S. exarator* as well. The wasp's presence can be detected even before the adult is seen by the exit holes in the wood. Apart from the large and conspicuous holes made by the woodworm there are also tiny, inconspicuous holes left by the wasps. In their larval stage they are completely dependent on their hosts — the woodworm larvae. The ratio of the numbers of woodworm to wasps is revealed by counting both types of exit holes: those left by the woodworm have yielded a live beetle, while a braconid exit hole indicates a beetle destroyed. *S. exarator* adults fly from May till September. In warm houses they often emerge in the winter months as well. They are usually seen on the window-panes or on the furniture where the females search for suitable places for oviposition, a process which may take several hours. While laying eggs the female inserts her vibrating ovipositor slowly into the wood. Although the ovipositor is very flexible, she can insert her eggs even in hard beechwood furniture. The eggs are rather large considering the female's slim body — about 1.5 mm long. The female therefore lays only a small number. She drills with her ovipositor into a tunnel in which a woodworm larva is hidden; on reaching the larva she paralyses it and inserts an egg. The braconid larva hatches out relatively quickly. During its life it ingests the whole woodworm larva (apart from a small amount of residue). The size of the braconid larva depends on the size of the host larva, i. e. on the quantity of food available. The larger the host larva, the larger not only the braconid larva but also the braconid imago. The parasite larva then spins a cocoon at the end of the woodworm's tunnel and pupates. The pupa of a future female is easily distinguished by its ovipositor projecting forward over the abdomen. The hatching adult first eats its way through the cocoon wall and then uses its mandibles to dig a narrow tunnel towards the surface of the wood.

S. exarator is very beneficial for even though it does not eliminate all the woodworm in a particular location, it has been found to account for more than 90 per cent of them.

S. exarator is common throughout Europe.
Length 5—9 mm.

1 ♀

2 ♂

3 ♀

Family: Braconidae

⊗ ***Apanteles glomeratus*** (L.) is probably the best-known member of this extensive genus; however, identifying the adult insect is not easy even for the expert. The imagines (**2, 3**) can easily be reared from the yellow cocoons grouped around a dead cabbage white butterfly caterpillar, most often the Large White (*Pieris brassicae*) (**1**).

The female of this braconid is very fertile and lays up to 2,000 eggs. She choses a future host for its larvae — usually a young cabbage white butterfly caterpillar — and with the help of her ovipositor injects 15 to 50 eggs into it, thus sentencing the caterpillar to a gradual death. The caterpillar cannot rid itself of these eggs which soon hatch into larvae; these feed on the caterpillar's haemolymph and its fat body. At first they avoid the internal organs so that the caterpillar's life is not endangered. The caterpillar has to be maintained alive for as long as it takes the parasite larvae in the body to develop. The young caterpillars show no signs at first of being slowly digested by the parasite but later a number of external symptoms begin to manifest themselves. In contrast to the greenish coloration of healthy caterpillars the infested caterpillar is yellowish and slow to react. Its body is also softer and the hind part thickens as the braconid larvae grow. The infested caterpillar can moult its larval skins normally but cannot pupate. While other healthy caterpillars are pupating, the parasite-infested caterpillar leaves the host plant and becomes stationary. In this last phase of their growth the braconid larvae devour the caterpillar's internal organs as well, so that only the skin is now left. Up to 50 small, whitish, legless larvae with yellowish heads appear almost immediately through minute exit holes in it. These larvae each spin a yellow cocoon about 4.5 mm by 1.5 mm on the dead caterpillar's body and pupate in it (**1**). The caterpillar with the yellow cocoons on its body is very conspicuous. The cocoons are often mistakenly called 'caterpillar eggs' and are still sometimes destroyed by ignorant vegetable growers along with the already dead caterpillar.

The numbers of infested cabbage white caterpillars in a locality varies. Sometimes more than 50 per cent are infested, at times as many as 90 per cent. Not only do the cabbage white butterfly caterpillars have parasites but their braconid parasites have their own parasites which can significantly reduce their numbers. There are dozens of species of these parasites' parasites, or hyperparasites. Most of these hyperparasites are chalcids or tiny species of ichneumons.

The importance of *A. glomeratus* is attested to by the fact that it was introduced from Europe into the USA as early as a century ago (1883) as a biological pest control in the fight against the cabbage white caterpillar.
Length 3—4 mm.

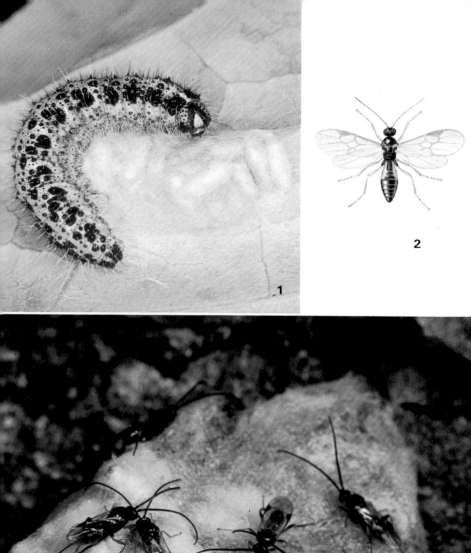

1

2

3

Family: Cynipidae — Gall Wasps

⊗ **Biorhiza pallida** (OL.) — Oak Apple Gall Wasp — produces two types of galls. Both are found on oak trees but each on a different part of the tree. Globular or potato-shaped galls (**1**) grow on branches, while smaller, round galls are found on the roots about 1 metre below the surface. Both males and females develop in the branch galls but only females in those on the roots.

The potato-like branch gall forms in the winter (December—February), when the gall wasp female uses its long, sturdy ovipositor to inject eggs into a bud on the oak branch. There the gall begins to develop; at first it is soft and pulpy and later spongy, being coloured whitish to yellowish, sometimes partly red. In the tiny gall cells begin to form in which the larvae will later develop. These cells give rise to an initial layer of tissue rich in nutrients (proteins, oils). Later a layer of carbohydrate is added. At this time the gall is about 4 mm in diameter. The larva is slowly growing within its cell, surrounded by an ample supply of nourishing food. Later the gall develops a secondary tissue layer which provides the larva with food until the end of its development. The gall is interwoven with the conducting fibres of phloems which reach into the larval cell tissues. In the fully developed gall the plant tissue becomes woody, especially around the larval cells. Because the cells are often tightly grouped together, a hard compact mass is created between them. The gall is fully grown about mid-June. The larva's development is finished by July and it pupates within its cell. Soon the gall wasps emerge, both males and females. There are marked differences between the sexes: the males have wings, the females are either wingless or with poorly developed wings. Only rarely do they have normal wings. Shortly after the gall wasps emerge, the gall dries out. The surface of the galls shows tiny exit holes of the adults and the larval cells can be clearly seen in cross-section (**2**). The fertilized females of this generation burrow into the ground and in the second half of July lay eggs in oak roots where the second type of gall later develops. This gall is almost spherical and whitish-red in colour. Sometimes these galls appear singly but most often they are joined in a cluster up to 50 mm in diameter, resembling a bunch of grapes. Unlike the fast-growing branch gall, this type of gall takes 16—18 months to develop. During the following winter the full-grown gall wasps leave their underground galls. They are all females, much larger than those of the summer generation and always wingless (**3, 4**). Until the whole life cycle of this species was discovered, this wingless gall wasp was considered a separate species and given the name *B. aptera* (*apterus* —wingless). The females of this generation lay unfertilized eggs in buds on oak branches; these buds then develop into potato-shaped galls. This two-generation life cycle takes two years. As in other galls, various tiny wasp species are parasitic on the gall wasps.

B. pallida is widespread through the greater part of Europe, Asia Minor and North Africa.

Diameter of branch gall 20—40 mm, underground root gall about 5 mm.
Length of agamous generation (♀) 3.5—6 mm, sexual generation ♂ 1.9—2.3 mm, ♀ 1.7—2.8 mm.

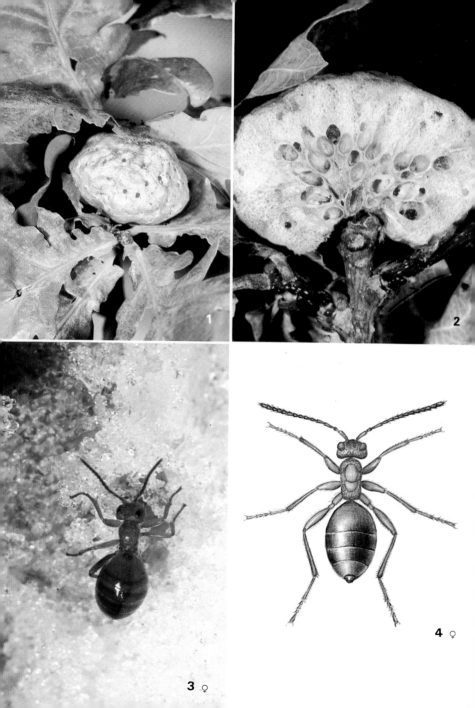

1

2

3 ♀

4 ♀

Family: Cynipidae — Gall Wasps

⊗ **Cynips quercusfolii** L. — the Cherry Gall Wasp — produces galls on various species of oak. Its leaf galls are a familiar sight. The wasp has also two generations, each of which develops in different types of gall: spherical galls on the underside of leaves and bud galls on the bark.

The spherical leaf galls, plentiful in some years, are mostly seen between July and October. The gall is attached to the leaf vein (either the main vein or one of the stronger side veins) by a very short stem. It is green-yellow at first (2), later turning yellow and then red on the side exposed to light (1). In the end it turns brown and wrinkled but remains on the leaf. The young gall is filled with fine cells containing a quantity of water; the old gall is spongy in texture. The gall contains a single larval chamber, about 3—4 mm in diameter, in which the whole of the gall wasp's development takes place (3). The larva feeds on the gall tissue and pupates in the chamber. The adult hatches in the winter, between December and February. It slowly chews its way through the gall tissue towards the surface and in favourable weather climbs out. These individuals are all females (4). They reproduce parthenogenetically, i. e. without fertilization. The female lays eggs in adventitious buds on the trunk and branches of oaks, where another type of gall starts to grow — a tiny, oval bud gall, red at first, later velvety purple. A larva develops inside it and eventually pupates. From these pupae tiny adults hatch out in May and June — both males and females. The fertilized females of this generation lay eggs in the leaf veins on the underside of leaves where they produce the above spherical galls. The cycle of two generations takes only a single year.

This species is widespraed throughout Europe and Asia Minor.

Diameter of spherical gall 10—20 mm (and more), length of bud gall about 3 mm; length of agamous generation (♀) 3.4—4 mm; sexual generation ♂ 2—2.5 mm, ♀ 2.3—2.7 mm.

⊗ **Cynips longiventris** HART. — Green Velvet Bud Gall Wasp — produces a very conspicuously coloured gall on the underside of the leaves of various species of oak (5).

The gall develops either on the main vein or a stronger side vein. Inside the gall there is a single chamber where the larva develops and pupates. The gall ripens in October and falls to the ground with the leaf in the autumn. The female tunnels towards the surface of the gall and in December bites her way through the surface layer and crawls out. She seeks out adventitious buds on tree trunks and branches and lays her eggs in them. The bud then changes into an oval gall, slightly pointed at the top. The gall colour is predominantly greenish-grey, thickly covered with white hairs. Inside the gall there is a single chamber in which the larva develops and eventually pupates. The gall ripens during May or June and the males and females emerge. To a large extent the adults resemble the previously described species but the leaf galls formed by the females of this sexual generation are so typical they cannot be mistaken for any other species.

C. longiventris is widespread in central, western and south-west Europe, in the southern parts of the USSR and in the Middle East.

Diameter of leaf gall 8—10 mm, length of bud gall 2 mm; length of agamous generation (♀) 2.9—3.6 mm, sexual generation ♂ 2—2.5 mm, ♀ 2.3—2.7 mm.

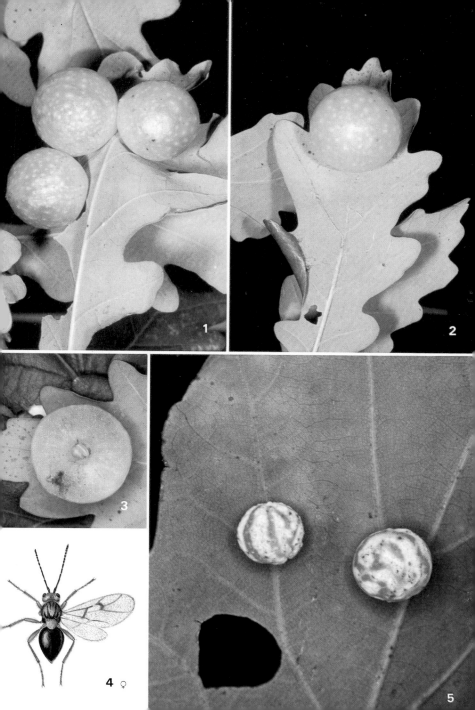

1

2

3

4 ♀

5

Family: Cynipidae — Gall Wasps

⊙ **Andricus coriarius** (HART.) produces very conspicuous and easily identifiable galls on the branches of various species of oak (1). They are brownish in colour, hard and non-sticky. They are irregular in shape and have various projections up to 10 mm long, reminiscent of cows' horns.

The galls of this species differ in internal construction from those produced by other species of this family. They do not contain a single chamber but a number of chambers. These are oval and the whole life cycle of these gall wasps takes place inside them. The galls ripen during September but remain on the branch. The imagines appear in late autumn and winter. So far only females have been recorded.

This warmth-loving wasp is widespread in central and southern Europe, Asia Minor and the Near East.

Diameter of gall up to 25 mm, length ♀ 3—4 mm.

⊗ **Andricus fecundator** (HTG.) produces characteristic cone-shaped formations on oak branches; the gall itself is hidden inside the cone. There is another type of gall in this wasp's life cycle — a tiny gall on the male oak catkins.

The cone-shaped gall appears in summer and autumn, most often in place of a side bud. It is green at first and the individual scales are tightly overlapped like roof tiles (2). Later it turns yellowish and then brown. In its last phase the cone opens out (3). It consists of up to 150 scales covered with fine hairs. The scales are not uniform in size or shape. The outer ones are broader and shorter than the inner ones. The inner gall grows inside the base of the cone. It is oval, pointed at one end, greenish-yellow at first, then reddish-brown. Inside it the larval and pupal developmental stages take place. Eventually the gall falls from the cone and its walls start to harden. In the autumn the cones also fall to the ground. A female wasp hatches out in spring, often, however, spending one more winter on the ground. She lays her eggs in the buds of future male catkins without having been fertilized (parthenogenetically). These eggs later produce very tiny, egg-shaped galls, green at first, light brown later. They ripen in May. While inside the galls, the future sexual generation (males and females) is changing from larva to pupa; the adults fly in June. The fertilized females of this generation lay their eggs singly in dormant buds. The buds change during the summer into cone-like galls.

This gall wasp is widespread in most of Europe and its range extends to the Middle East.

Length of cone 20—30 mm, inner gall 6—10 mm, length of gall in male catkin about 2.2 mm; length of agamous generation (♀) 4.3—4.8 mm, sexual generation ♂ 1.5—1.6 mm, ♀ 1.6—1.9 mm.

Family: Cynipidae — Gall Wasps

⊗ *Andricus kollari* (HART.) — Marble Gall Wasp — belongs to a relatively common and widespread species. It may be less common than *Cynips quercusfolii* but its galls can be seen from a distance (*C. quercusfolii* galls are hidden on the underside of oak leaves). It also produces two very different types of gall. Particularly conspicuous and unmistakable are the galls in which agamous females develop. They are produced on the end or side buds of young branches of various species of oak. Their growth does not interfere with that of the buds. The agamous female's gall is spherical, smooth, sometimes with little protrusions. At first it is greenish and covered in fine down. With time its colour changes via light ochre to brownish and the surface becomes hairless. The gall gradually hardens. This type of gall grows most often on low oaks which are not thriving due to either poor soil (e.g. alongside forest parhs) or other detrimental factors. Often there are many galls growing close together and leaves appear between them (1). The gall contains a slightly elongate larval chamber, lined with a thin protective layer. The whole development of the larva and pupa takes place in this chamber. The galls mature in August, sometimes even later. The agamous female drills her way to the surface and leaves the gall through a round exit hole. In colour and other physical attributes she resembles several other gall wasp species (e.g. *Andricus lignicola, A. calyciformis,* etc.) so closely that they can only be distinguished by the agamous galls. Often various commensals and parasites (even other gall wasps) develop in these galls. Two or three galls often fuse together, creating an irregular shape.

The unfertilized agamous female forms a different type of gall. These tiny, inconspicuous bud galls are brownish-yellow to greyish in colour, oval and slightly grainy in appearance. They grow on either the axillary or terminal buds of the young twigs of Turkey Oak. Several galls usually form in a single bud. These galls are difficult to distinguish from similar galls made by other species. They ripen in April. The fertilized female of this generation lays her eggs in buds, so founding the agamous generation described above.

This gall wasp is most common in central, southern and western Europe. It also occurs in the British Isles, in North Africa and Asia Minor

Diameter of spherical agamous gall 10—25, sometimes up to 33 mm, length of bud gall (winter) 2—3 mm, width 2 mm; length of agamous generation (♀) 4.8—6 mm, sexual generation (♂, ♀) about 2 mm.

⊙ *Andricus hungaricus* (HART.) produces one of the largest and most conspicuous oak galls. The sturdy, irregular-surfaced gall (3) encloses a small (only about 4—5 mm) inner gall, in which the future imago develops (2). The gall ripens in the autumn and falls to the ground but the adults (females) only hatch out in February or March of the next year.

This warmth-loving gall wasp is widespread and sometimes common in central and south-west Europe.

Diameter of gall up to 40 mm; length ♀ 3.8—5.3 mm.

Family: Cynipidae — Gall Wasps

⊗ **Andricus lignicola** (HART.). — Cola-nut Gall Wasp — produces spherical galls which grow from axillary and less often, terminal buds on the branches of various species of oak. The inner tissue of the gall is pinkish-red. The galls are very firm, woody and their colouring changes during the growth. Sometimes they occur singly, in other cases groups of galls grow close together (1). Inside the gall there is a flattened larval chamber in which the gall wasp develops. The chamber lies near the base of the gall, in the place where the gall is attached to the host plant. The gall ripens in late summer and remains on the branch through the winter. The adults (agamous females) do not appear until June and July of the following year. In colour and other physical characteristics they so closely resemble several other gall wasps that the species can only be safely identified by the galls.

The agamout females (2) lay unfertilized eggs in axillar or terminal buds of oak branches. Inside these buds develop tiny galls which ripen in February. The adults (males and females) hatch out in March and April. After fertilization the female founds another generation which develops in spherical galls.
This gall wasp is widespread through almost all of Europe.
Diameter of spherical gall 8—10 mm, length of sexual generation gall 2 mm; length of agamous generation (♀) 4—4.5 mm, sexual generation (♂, ♀) 2 mm.

⊗ **Andricus quercuscalicis** (BURGSD.) — Knopper Gall Wasp — also produces two different types of gall. The galls growing on acorns are well known. They are green and very sticky at first, later becoming brown and hard. The gall is irregularly shaped; although small in some cases, in others it may cover the whole acorn (3). Its surface is covered by 5—8 longitudinal, irregularly twisted ridges. The inside is hollow and the structure has a small round apical aperture. At the bottom of this cavity lies the inner ellipsoid gall in which the adult develops. Sometimes there are two or more inner galls. In early autumn (i. e. late August) the gall falls from the tree together with the acorn. The imago is fully grown by November but does not emerge from the gall until the next February or March. It may, however, remain in the gall for another year. From these galls emerge red- and yellow-coloured females, very similar to those of several other species. Without fertilization they found a future generation which develops in galls placed in the axis of the male catkins of Turkey Oaks. The catkin galls are oval and very smooth. Greenish at first, they become a matt brown later. The wasps develop quickly; the tiny individuals of the sexual generation fly in May. The fertilized females then found another generation which develops in the acorn galls.

This gall wasp is widespread in southern, western and central Europe and Asia Minor; it was first recorded in Britain as late as 1959 and has since become very widespread and common.
Height of acorn gall 15—20 mm, width 18—25 mm, length of oak catkin gall 1—2 mm; length of agamous generation (♀) up to 5 mm, sexual generation (♀) 1.3—1.5 mm.

Family: Cynipidae — Gall Wasps

⊗ **Neuroterus quercusbaccarum** (L.) — Common Spangle Gall Wasp (in earlier literature referred to as *N. lenticularis*) — develops on oaks. This gall wasp also produces two different types of galls. The rather conspicuous lens-shaped gall grows from July onwards on the underside of leaves **(1)**. There are usually many galls on one leaf, sometimes dozens. The gall is flat-bottomed and slightly convex above. With the help of a magnifying glass one can discern a short stem connecting it to the leaf. It is usually yellowish-green or reddish in colour, covered with white hairs which later become reddish or brownish **(2)**. The larva feeds on the gall tissue from its chamber inside the gall. In the autumn the gall falls to the ground and remains among the fallen leaves until the spring. It needs humidity: the originally rather flat shape becomes more distended. The larva grows slowly inside the gall and in March it pupates. From the pupae in these spangle galls only females hatch. These lay unfertilized eggs in oak buds. The next generation develops in spherical juicy galls, which are best seen in the spring on the underside of leaves and in male catkins. The spherical galls also contain larvae which after pupation hatch out as either males or females in June. The fertilized females lay their eggs in June and July on the underside of oak leaves where the lens-shaped galls gradually develop. Both generations occur in a single year.

    N. quercusbaccarum inhabits a large part of Europe, Asia Minor and North Africa.

Diameter of lens-shaped gall 5—6 mm, height 2 mm, diameter of spherical gall 5—8 mm; length of agamous generation (♀) 2.5—2.8 mm, sexual generation ♂ 2.7—2.9 mm, ♀ 2.5—2.8 mm.

⊗ **Neuroterus numismalis** (Geoffr.) — Silk-button Spangle Gall Wasp — develops similarly to the above species. It also produces two very different types of gall; both grow on oak leaves. The cup-shaped gall is very conspicuous and common **(3)**, growing on the underside of the leaf. It is flat at first but later a ridge appears round the periphery and the centre becomes concave. The whole gall is densely covered with silky brownish hairs. Its is attached to the leaf by a short stalk. One leaf can carry several dozen or even hundreds of galls. The galls overwinter on the ground amongst the fallen leaves. The larvae inside pupate and the females hatch out in March. There are no males in this generation. These females lay their eggs inside the larger oak buds. Later the other, less conspicuous type of gall appears on the leaves. It is flat on the underside and slightly convex above. The larval and pupal development is completed by late May or early June when the adults hatch (males and females; this generation was originally considered to be a separate species and called *Neuroterus vesicator*). The fertilized females of this generation lay their eggs on the underside of leaves where the cup-shaped galls form. Both generations occur in the same year.

    N. numismalis is widespread in a large part of Europe and Asia Minor.

Diameter of cup-shaped and round gall about 3 mm; length of agamous generation (♀) 2—2.7 mm, sexual generation ♂ 2 mm, ♀ 0.9—1.2 mm.

Family: Cynipidae — Gall Wasps

⊗ **Diplolepis rosae** (L.) — Bedeguar Gall Wasp — is the most common of several species of European gall wasps which produce galls on rose plants. The gall of *D. rosae*, known as the bedeguar or Robin's pincushion gall, can be recognized at a distance on Dog Rose bushes in summer and early autumn. It grows most often on leaves, leaf stems or young shoots, rarely on flowers or fruits. It is covered in long, tangled, branched greenish, reddish or yellowish hair **(1)**. The galls vary in size; sometimes several galls grow into a single mass and the whole is approximately fist-sized. Unchanged or slightly changed leaves often grow out of the gall. With large galls which need a great deal of nourishment during growth the shoot dies away above the gall so that the gall is left at the top of the branch.

Both the gall and the life cycle of *D. rosae* differ markedly from other species. Inside the gall a larva develops in its chamber. This chamber is lined with tiny, thin-walled cells, rich in oils and proteins which nourish the larva. The smaller galls usually contain only a single larval chamber. Large compound galls contain several larval chambers **(2)**. The larva finishes its growth inside the gall and pupates; the pupa overwinters. In the autumn the gall changes both in colour and texture. The fresh hairs dry up, turn brown and the gall hardens and remains on the plant as a dark, irregular lump. In the spring of the next year the gall wasps emerge. These are usually only females. Males are rare — the ratio is one male to several hundred females.

Adult gall wasps are occasionally seen but it is much easier to rear them from galls cut off a rose bush in the spring and kept humid (they must not be allowed to dry out). We must be careful when the adults hatch as these galls are not inhabited solely by *D. rosae* but also by a number of parasites. Very often these are tiny wasps (mostly of the super-families Chalcidoidea, Proctotrupoidea, etc.).

D. rosae is widespread throughout Europe.

Length 3.7—4.3 mm.

Family: Torymidae

⊗ **Torymus bedeguaris** (L.) is a constant companion of *Diplolepis rosae*. Green, blue and purple predominate in its colouring; the beauty of its metallic colour and the fine sculpturing of the body surface can best be appreciated under a microscope. Its wings are very delicate and their venation reduced. The female **(3)** bears a long ovipositor. When laying eggs, she has to reach inside the bedeguar chamber where the larva of *D. rosae* lives. The egg is laid inside this larva and feeds on its tissue; eventually it pupates in the gall. The male **(4)** has no ovipositor.

The adults of *T. bedeguaris* can easily be reared from bedeguar galls, like their hosts. Dozens of individuals can hatch out of a single gall.

T. bedeguaris is widespread in a large part of Europe.

Length 4 mm.

3 ♀

4 ♂

Family: Cynipidae — Gall Wasps

⊗ ***Diplolepis eglanteriae*** (HART.) — Smooth Pea Gall Wasp — produces only a single type of gall; it does not alternate between two different galls or two generations. The galls occur on various rose species almost everywhere. The gall is spherical, with a smooth surface. It is green in colour, often reddish, and later changes to brownish. It is attached to the host plant by a minute stalk. It is most common on the underside of leaves but is also commonly found on the upper side. Its presence cannot be detected from the opposite side of the leaf. The galls are often grouped closely together (1) and the gall may sit on one of the main leaf veins. At other times they can grow on the area between the veins, on leaf stalks, thorns or bark. The galls have even been found on the hairs of a bedeguar caused by *Diplolepis rosae* on rose plants. Inside the gall there is a single chamber in which the adult develops. The gall ripens in summer and often falls off at the slightest touch.

The adults hatch in May or June of the following year. When the gall is irregularly shaped and has more than one chamber, it contains commensals.

This wasp's gall resembles that of *D. centifoliae* which, however, is covered with pointed papillae.

D. eglanteriae is distributed throughout a large part of Europe.
Diameter of gall 3—5 mm; length ♂ 2.5—3 mm, ♀ 2.7—3.3 mm.

⊗ ***Diastrophus rubi*** (BOUCHÉ) also produces only a single type of gall and therefore only a single generation each year. The gall of this wasp is very conspicuous; it occurs mainly on the stems of blackberry and raspberry (2), more rarely on the petioles. The petiole galls are tiny and usually contain only one to three chambers. The stem gall is smooth, with no cracks. It contains a number of oval larval chambers, each measuring about 2.5—3 mm, which can be seen as irregular bulges on the gall surface. The chambers are best seen in cross-section (3). Each holds a white legless larva which eventually pupates.

The adults emerge in May of the following year and fly until June. The female lays her eggs in blackberry and raspberry canes where the gall described above develops. The stems of the infested plants are fragile, dry up and bear little fruit. Tiny chalcids are frequent parasites on the larvae of this gall wasp.

D. rubi is widespread in almost all of Europe.
Length of gall 15—80 mm or even more, width 5—10 mm; length ♂ 2—2.2 mm, ♀ 2.3—2.8 mm.

Family: Aphelinidae

⊗ **Aphelinus mali** (HALD.) is the main parasite of the aphid *Eriosoma lanigerum*. This tiny insect **(1)** originates in the USA. When its beneficial effect on limiting aphid infestations was discovered, it was introduced into other fruit-growing regions outside America. It reached Europe in 1920 and has since spread both with and without man's help.

The adults are difficult to collect in their natural habitats but can easily be reared from colonies of aphids. They usually run; they can only fly a short distance but may be carried by the wind for miles. The female lays between 50 and 100 eggs during her lifetime. She pierces the aphid's skin with her ovipositor and inserts a single egg. The egg is exceptionally large; its length is a quarter to a sixth of that of the female's body. Oviposition takes place quickly — the female rarely needs more than one minute to accomplish it. The infested aphid turns black. The larva in its body feeds on its tissues and finally pupates. After the adult parasite has made an exit hole, the dry aphid skin remains stuck to the plant. There are 6—10 generations each year: their number depends on the temperature of the locality which also influences the speed of the development from egg to imago.

A. mali is a proven enemy of the *E. lanigerum* aphid. This aphid is the only host of *A. mali.* This species has been used successfully in biological pest control programmes in many countries.
Length 0.8—1.3 mm.

⊗ **Aphytis mytilaspidis** (LE BAR.) was discovered over a century ago in America, where it hatched out of the scale insect *Lepidosaphes ulmi.* More detailed study of its life cycle revealed that its larva does not develop only in *L. ulmi* but also in a number of other diaspidid species. *A. mytilaspidis* **(2)** can be easily reared from colonies of *L. ulmi.* A section of branch infested by the communally feeding. *L. ulmi* (they are common on apple, willow, etc.), kept in a vessel covered with nylon mesh, will soon produce various tiny parasites which usually include these tiny yellow wasps. Because of climatic conditions, there are usually only two generations a year in Europe. The female finds a suitable host; first she explores its scale with her antennae, then pierces the scale with her ovipositor and lays her egg on the surface of the host. The larva is rather broad; it remains on the host's body (it is ectophagous), slowly consuming it. Most of the adults are females; males are less numerous and in some localities absent altogether. The adults move actively only for short distances but can be carried further by the wind.

This tiny wasp is a natural predator of the scale-insect of the Diaspididae family.

It is widespread over a large part of the Palaearctic and Nearctic region.
Length 0.7—1.3 mm.

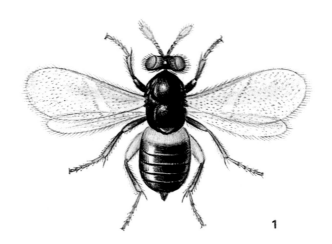

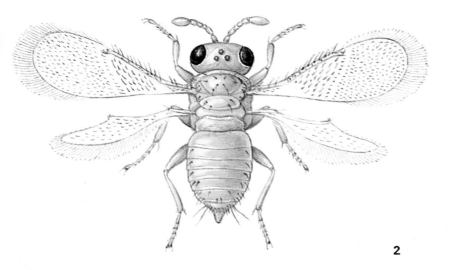

1

2

Family: Scoliidae

⊙ **Scolia maculata** (Dʀ.) is one of the largest European Hymenoptera. There are differences between the males and the females. The female **(1)** is more robust, with a large head, 12-segmented antennae and a sting connected to poison glands. The male has a small head, long and straight 13-segmented antennae, and no sting. The adults are very warmth-loving; they fly in the daytime and seek out the flowers of various shrubs and herbaceous plants, from which they obtain nectar. They have biting-sucking mouthparts adapted for this purpose.

The remarkable development of this giant wasp takes place at the expense of *Oryctes nasicornis*. The female of *Scolia maculata* can lay eggs within a few hours of mating. First she has to find the beetle larva, which feeds on decomposed wood in the ground. When she finds it, she burrows towards it, using her mandibles and fore legs, and injects venom into its body with her sting. The beetle larva, thus paralysed, is rendered immobile and changes into a living convenience food which stays fresh for the whole period of the wasp's development. After stinging the host larva, the female cleans it and rids it of any ectoparasites. Eventually she sticks a single egg on the larva's underside. The hatched wasp larva bites open the skin of its host, inserts its head and feeds on the host's body tissue and fluids. The development has to be fast enough for the paralysed beetle larva not to deteriorate. The wasp larva moults three times during its development. It is legless and sturdy, with a small head. When fully grown, it spins a silk cocoon in its underground chamber, overwinters and pupates in the spring. The adults appear in early June and are on the wing until early August.

As the host beetle has become rare, this beautiful wasp is no longer common. It inhabits Europe (with the exception of the north), as far as the Causasus, Central Asia and North Africa. It occurs in three forms within this large territory. Length ♂ 26—32 mm, ♀ 32—40 mm.

⊙ **Scolia quadripunctata** F. is often referred to as *S. sexmaculata*. Both scientific names originate in the number of light spots on the dorsal side of the abdomen. Most individuals only have 4 spots **(2)** but there can be 6, 8 or, in exceptional cases, 10 and in males even only 2. According to the number of spots the individual forms were designated *bipunctata* (with 2 spots), *sexpunctata* (6 spots), *octopunctata* (8 spots) and *decempunctata* (10 spots).

It is an essentially warmth-loving species, inhabiting woodlands and grasslands. The males appear about 10—12 days before the females. The adults visit various flowering plants, e.g. Wild Thyme, Spiked Speedwell, *Orlaya grandiflora*, Wild Angelica, etc., for nectar. They spend the night in burrows several centimetres deep in the ground. On cold days they do not emerge at all; only in temperatures around 20 °C do they appear on flowering plants. Their development is similar to the preceding species and other Scoliidae. The female uses a wide variety of hosts, namely the larvae of scarabaeid beetles, e.g. *Anoxia, Anomala, Anisoplia, Epicometis, Oxythyrea, Cetonia* and *Liocola*.

S. quadripunctata inhabits a large part of Europe except for northern regions, Asia Minor and North Africa.
Length ♂ 9—14 mm, ♀ 10—15 mm.

1 ♀

2

Family: Chrysididae

⊙ *Chrysis nitidula* F. is predominantly greenish-blue or blue in colour **(1)**. It can tolerate cooler environments and hence may be found at higher altitudes. Like all other Chrysididae, it likes the sun. It flies from June till August and likes to sit on the warm wooden walls of old barns and haylofts. The larva is parasitic; it develops in the nests of some potter wasps and solitary bees.

It inhabits a large part of Europe, the Caucasus, Siberia and Central Asia.
Length 7—13 mm.

⊗ *Chrysis ignita* L. is very variable in size, colouring and surface sculpturing, thus many forms have been described, often as different species. It appears that there are no two individuals the same. It is said that experts can recognize from the overall appearance of the adult in which host the larva developed.

The adults **(2,4)** occur from spring to autumn and can be seen taking nectar from flowering Umbelliferae. They often sun themselves on warm wooden walls, fences, etc. They are also found in mountainous regions.

The development of *C. ignita* is complicated. The female seeks out the nests of various Hymenoptera, mainly potter wasps, sometimes solitary bees, and lays her eggs in them. She may, of course, be attacked by the nest owner while doing this, but she is saved from their sting by her thick body armour and her ability to curl up into a ball. The larva of *C. ignita* develops in the nest at the potter wasp larva's expense. Occasionally it feeds on the provisions (various insect larvae) which the potter wasp had amassed for her offspring.

C. ignita is widespread throughout the whole of Europe (as far as Scandinavia), North Africa and temperate Asia.
Length 4—13 mm.

⊗ *Chrysis cyanea* (L.) **(3)** is relatively common in sunny places where it flies from May until end of summer. It may also be found in mountainous regions. It often sits on wooden buildings and sun-warmed walls, telegraph poles, wooden fences, etc.

The female seeks out the nests of solitary bees and lays her eggs in them. The most frequent hosts of this species are solitary wasps of the genus *Trypoxylon* and mason wasps of the genera *Osmia* and *Odynerus*. A blind larva hatches from the egg. It is legless but moves by using two protrusions at the posterior end of its body. It feeds on the body tissue of its host. In a nest of the *Trypoxylon,* the chrysidid larva initially feeds alongside the wasp larva on the accumulation of paralysed spiders. When this food supply is exhausted, the parasite larva turns its attention to the host larva. The grown larva exudes a special liquid from its mouthparts, which quickly solidifies on contact with air into a silky fibre. The larva spins a cup-shaped cocoon with a recessed lid, where it pupates. If the cocoon is discovered by an ichneumon female, she lays her eggs in it. In this case the ichneumon is a hyperparasite (parasite's parasite).

C. cyanea is widespread in a large part of Europe (up to 64° north), Siberia, Asia Minor and the Caucasus.
Length 3.5—8 mm.

Family: Mutillidae — Velvet Wasps

⊗ **Mutilla europaea** L. The males and females differ considerably. The male **(1)** always has two pairs of membranous wings, 13-segmented antennae, three ocelli on the head, a segmented thorax and a 7-segmented abdomen. The female **(2)**, on the other hand, is wingless, her antennae are shorter and only 12-segmented, she has no ocelli, her thorax is differently constructed from that of the male and her abdomen is only 6-segmented. Of all these differences the presence of wings is the most obvious distinguishing feature between male and female.

M. europaea inhabits well-vegetated, dry areas in both lowlands and uplands. The males frequent flowering Umbelliferae, while the females move about rapidly on the ground. Their colour combination strongly resembles the beetle *Thanasimus formicarius* (L.). However, anyone under the impression they have collected a beetle will soon realize their error when they feel the painful sting.

When M. europaea was found in a bumblebee's nest almost 200 years ago, it was thought to be merely a case of cohabitation. Later, however, M. europaea was found to be more than an innocent cohabitee. Its larva is an arch-enemy of bumblebee larvae. M. europaea is not particular which host species it chooses for the development of its future offspring. Its larvae can develop in the nests of a wide variety of bumblebee species. The female enters the bumblebee nest and lays her eggs, one in each brood cell, where a bumblebee larva is developing. She does not kill the bumblebee larva, because it provides the food for her own larva during its brief life. It pupates in the nest and eventually emerges as an adult. The more food is available to the larva during its development, the bigger it grows, hence resulting in a larger adult. This is why there is considerable variation in size among adult mutillids. If a large number of eggs are laid in a bumblebee's nest, the colony can be noticeably weakened. In such weakened colonies the mutillids can outnumber the hatched bumblebees.

Both male and female mutillids have a stridulation apparatus between their abdominal tergites with which they produce sounds. These sounds are only barely audible to the human ear and the mutillids produce them when irritated.

M. europaea is widespread throughout the Palaearctic region.
Length ♂ 11—17 mm, ♀ 10—16 mm.

⊗ **Mutilla marginata** Baer appears to be the most common of European Mutillidae **(3, 4)**. It resembles the preceding species but its thorax is twice as long as it is wide and is also narrower than the head.

M. marginata inhabits well-vegetated, dry places and is commonest in foothills and mountain regions. Its way of life is probably similar to that of M. europaea but has not been researched in detail.

It inhabits a large part of Europe and Asia Minor.
Length ♂ 11—15 mm, ♀ 10—15 mm.

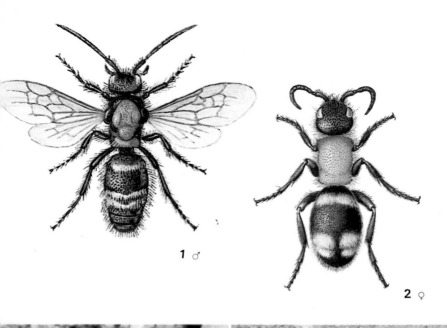

Family: Formicidae — Ants

☉ **Polyergus rufescens** LATR. is distinguished by its reddish coloration and its narrow, pointed sabre-like mandibles. The mandibles differ from the serrated mandibles of other ants, being more like those of some beetles. These mandibles are weapons of aggression.

P. rufescens is quite a common species, preferring sunny, warm habitats on sandy soil or limestone. Its raider's life-style has earned it the nickname 'the Amazon Ant'. It lives a remarkable life, quite different from that of other ants. Not only is it unable to build a nest but neither can it feed itself or look after its offspring. It is totally dependent on the help of slaves of another species and has to have a constant supply of them (1). Through evolution it has developed a raider's instinct. It steals pupae from the nests of *Formica fusca* and other species. From these pupae workers (slaves) soon hatch. *P. rufescens* does not steal larvae or eggs because it cannot rear them. The Amazon Ants organize these raids with great efficiency; they have become essential to their survival. The raids usually take place in the late afternoon in July and August. The ants leave their nest, run around for a while and then slowly line up in a snake-line formation, several centimetres wide and up to several metres long. It contains thousands of ants. They walk in a line and the whole regiment remains more or less the same width throughout the expedition. It is an unforgettable sight, winding on and on like a red snake until it reaches the anthill — the object of the raid. There is always a fight but the victory of the strong and aggressive Amazon Ants against the weaker ants is a foregone conclusion. The Amazon Ants (3) use their pointed mandibles in the attack. They bite the heads off the defending ants or sink their mandibles into their head capsules. They steal the pupae and carry them home in their mandibles; the number of pupae stolen may be many thousands. The Amazon Ants carry out their raids up to tens of metres away from their nests but always unerringly find their way home.

They swarm at midday in summer. At this time winged males (4) and females (2) emerge from the anthill. The male perishes after the mating flight but the female sheds her wings and founds a new colony, of course by violent means. She penetrates the anthill of another species, kills the resident queen and gradually takes over the nest. In the spring she lays her eggs. The hatched larvae are looked after by the resident workers. As the original nest has lost its own queen, the number of workers does not increase in the normal way. However, the lack of workers would endanger the running and even the existence of the Amazon Ant colony, so the Amazons obtain new workers by raiding other anthills. The number of slaves in a colony is many times that of the number of Amazon Ants. A young nest contains about 150 Amazon Ants and over three times that number of slaves. A large nest of 2,000 to 3,000 Amazon Ants can contain up to 10,000 slaves.

Amazon Ants inhabit a large part of the temperate Holarctic region.
Length ☿ 5—7 mm, ♀ 8—9 mm, ♂ 6—7 mm.

2 ♀

3 ☿

4 ♂

Family: Formicidae — Ants

⊗ *Lasius fuliginosus* (LATR.) has a strongly emarginate top of the head. It is a diurnal species which inhabits deciduous and mixed woodlands, parks and orchards mainly in lowland localities but can also be found in mountainous regions. Although it prefers dry habitats, often living in sand dunes, it lives in damp places as well. It has a characteristic smell.

The nest of *L. fuliginosus* is unique among the European ants. It is a so-called carton nest; it hangs freely in a hollow tree (poplar, willow etc.), under tree roots, in old tree stumps **(1)** or exceptionally under stones. It may last as long as 20 years and more. Because it is so well hidden, few people ever see it in nature. The workers **(3)** build it from coarse wood pulp and soil particles which they stick together with honeydew and the secretions of their mandibular glands. A fragile structure gradually forms, reminiscent of a brown or black sponge. This nest is sometimes compared to that of the hornet but the building techniques are quite different. The carton nest is connected to its surroundings by paths which could be called ant trails. The ants keep them clean; they remove all stones, twigs and other obstacles from the path of the workers hurrying in search of food or returning home. The traffic is busy in both directions. Often there are several carton nests close together — these have been originated by groups splitting off from the original nest. All the nests are connected by trails, all together measuring tens of metres. After a certain time each nest becomes autonomous. Apart from the nests and trails, the workers also construct soil tunnels on the surface. They build them at the busiest sections of their roads and around aphids or scale insects on plants, mainly oaks. Aphids are well-known producers of the sweet excretion, honeydew, which the ants eagerly lick **(2)** and which represents a significant part of their food. The tunnels protect the donors of this sweet liquid from attack by predatory or parasitic insects and from the elements. Apart from honeydew, the ants feed on the larvae of various insects. They complement their food with fungal hyphae which grow through the walls of the nest and give them a velvety appearance. The fungus feeds on the honeydew which the ants bring into the nest.

The males and females of *L. fuliginosus* swarm in June and July, often in very large numbers **(1)**. After mating the female sheds her wings and either enters a nest of her own species or founds a new one — the future anthill — by violent means. She enters the nest of another species (e. g. *L. niger*) which has no female; or if it has, she defeats it and becomes the ruling queen. She lays eggs but does not look after her offspring; the original inhabitants of the nest take care of them. The numbers of the original inmates gradually decrease and the descendants of the intruder begin to outnumber them, until in the course of several years they become the only inhabitants. The colony is monogynous or oligogynous (with a small number of queens). *L. fuliginosus* sometimes shares the same tree with other ant species but each species keeps to their own part of the tree.

L. fuliginosus occurs throughout Europe, the Caucasus, Siberia, China, Japan and the western part of India.

Length ☿ 4—6 mm, ♀ 5—6.8 mm, ♂ 3.8—5.2 mm.

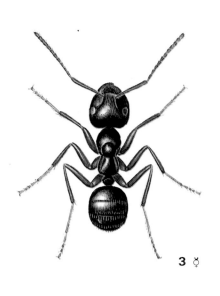

2 ☿ ☿

3 ☿

Family: Formicidae — Ants

⊗ *Lasius flavus* (F.) is one of the small, common species. The workers **(2)** are pale yellow, the females **(3)** brown and the males brownish-black. They may be confused with another similarly coloured *Myrmica* species but in *L. flavus* the petiole is one-segmented and there is no sting. They defend themselves by biting through the victim's skin and squirting a little formic acid from their abdomen into the wound.

L. flavus is not particular in its choice of place to found and build its nest. It can be a dry locality or a damp and swampy one. We often find it in damp meadows, on forest edges, in grassy ditches, on the banks of streams, in dry places, in fields, vineyards and gardens. It only avoids the dark interior of woods and does not enter houses. It is common from the lowlands to the mountains.

Above the underground nest, which reaches some 40 centimetres in depth, there is usually an earthy mound up to 30 centimetres high, covered with vegetation. It is closed; there are no connecting paths leading to its immediate environment. Sometimes these mounds are over 50 centimetres high **(1)**. In meadows, where this ant is most common, they present a problem for both hand-scythes and mechanical mowers. Sometimes *L. flavus* builds a nest under a stone, in a rotting tree stump or under the bark of a tree. It may share the same stone with ants of other species.

L. flavus lives almost exclusively underground and its senses have developed accordingly. Its eyesight is very weak and hunting and moving are guided mainly by smell. The main food is honeydew, exuded by aphids living on grass roots. The ants look after and protect the aphids. Occasionally they take animal food — insects in various stages of development.

The males and females of *L. flavus* swarm in the afternoon in July and August and sometimes in September and October. At this time, the ants make holes in the earth mound and crawl out: the males and females to make their mating flight, the workers in attendance. After the mating flight the female sheds her wings. Her next task is to found a new nest. She founds it by herself, without the help of another species. She makes a chamber in the ground, overwinters in it and in the spring begins to lay eggs. Sometimes several females occupy the same chamber and start looking after their offspring at the same time but as soon as the first worker hatches, the females begin to fight. Because *L. flavus* is monogynous, the victorious female does not tolerate another female during the period of workers hatching. Only one can become the queen of the future nest and she will subdue all the workers.

L. flavus is not aggressive. If its nest is attacked, it defends itself but prefers to withdraw into the safety of its underground chambers.

It is widespread in Europe and temperate Asia. It is also common in Africa and the eastern part of North America.

Length ⚨ 1.7—4 mm, ♀ 7—9 mm, ♂ 3—4 mm.

1

2 ☿

3 ♀

Family: Formicidae — Ants

⊗ **Lasius niger** (L.) is not black, as its scientific name suggests, but brown. It is one of our most common ants. It has no special demands as to its habitat; it inhabits both dry and damp places from lowlands to mountains. It is also common in gardens, meadows and in house walls. It avoids shady woods.

The nest is monogynous and L. niger builds it in various places, very often under a stone. If the locality is lacking in stones, it nests in the ground, in old tree stumps or under tree bark **(1,2)**. The underground nest is connected to the outside by tiny openings surrounded by minute mounds of earth which can often be seen on country paths. There is usually an earthen superstructure piled round grass stems above the underground nest. The workers **(4)** build this superstructure from tiny grains of soil stuck together with saliva. The resulting particles can be bigger than the workers. They also ensure that the mound is not too overgrown with grass. The underground nest and the superstructure are interconnected by a complex tunnel system. The building is firm and resistant to winds and summer rain; however, the persistent autumn rains and snow eventually destroy it.

Mating swarms are in July and August, often in large numbers. The female **(5)** sheds her wings shortly after mating. She founds the new nest by herself, without the help of any other ant species. She encloses herself in the maternal chamber, which she never again leaves. Here she lays her eggs and rears the first larvae **(3)**. L. niger workers eat the sweet honeydew exuded by aphids and scale insects. Not only do they 'rear' them, they also cover them over with earthen galleries to protect them from natural enemies while sitting on the plants. These galleries are reached by partly open, partly covered trails. L. niger also feeds on insects, nectar and seeks out sweet foods in houses. The larvae are able to eat solid food. The female's life expectancy is about 15 years and the worker's about 7 years.

L. niger is widespread from Europe through temperate Asia to North America. It also lives in North Africa and has been introduced into southern Africa.
Length ☿ 2—5 mm, ♀ 6.6—10 mm, ♂ 3.5—4.7 mm.

☉ **Lasius emarginatus** (Oliv.) is distinctly bi-coloured; its red and yellow thorax contrasts with the brown head and abdomen **(6)**. It likes warm, dry conditions and avoids damp places. It nests mainly in rocky biotopes, especially rock fissures and cavities, but also at the edges of woods. It is also to a certain extent a 'domestic' species as it is common in gardens and houses in both town and country. It inhabits cracks between stones in walls and sometimes it lives in dead wood. In the south it builds a type of carton nest.

Males and females swarm at night between June and August. The workers are predatory and hunt caterpillars and other insects but they also eat honeydew. They are also partial to the oily protuberances of the seeds of some plants, e.g. the Dog Violet. They colect and carry these seeds into the nest, but on the way many seeds are lost and so the ants contribute to the dispersal of the plant to places the seeds would not otherwise reach.

L. emarginatus occurs mainly in central and southern Europe but also in South-West Asia.
Length ☿ 3—4 mm, ♀ 7—9 mm, ♂ 3.2—4.2 mm.

4 ♀ 5 ♀ 6 ☿

Family: Formicidae — Ants

⊗ **Formica polyctena** FÖRST. is slightly smaller than *F. rufa* which it resembles both in shape and colour. It used to be classed as a mere variant of *F. rufa* but in time was discovered to be a species in its own right. Today the coloration of individual workers is not taken as a main distinguishing feature as it can by very variable even within the same nest. The most important, although not immutable, feature is the distribution of hairs on the head, thorax and petiolar scale. In *F. polyctena* the head, thorax and scale are hairless, while in *F. rufa* they are covered with a multitude of fine hairs. The two species are indistinguishable to the naked eye.

F. *polyctena* lives mostly in spruce woods but also inhabits deciduous woods, especially their sunny margins. Its lifestyle is — apart from some differences in behaviour — similar to that of *F. rufa*. It builds extensive mounds above the ground, usually around tree stumps, but the base of its nest always lies well underground. This is why this type of nest (like those of similar species) is called a combined nest (see illustration). The building material is usually spruce needles, sometimes fine twigs. The needle pile is very important to the ants' lifestyle because it forms a reservoir of thermal energy. The nest is quite large; it can be several metres in circumference. It is inhabited, as in most ants, by three castes which differ in morphology, physiology and behaviour. The most numerous are the workers — always wingless, sexually immature females; the females and males are less abundant. In most cases the nest is polygynous, which means it is inhabited by a large number (up to several thousands) of queens. A monogynous nest with only one queen is rare. The young queen has two pairs of smoky-coloured wings which she sheds after mating.

Before the arrival of winter the ants retreat to a depth of 1.5—2 metres. There they remain motionless in small groups until the spring. In the first days of March, when the anthill is warmed by the sun, the workers and queens crawl out onto the surface. They sun themselves, set out to look for food and start working on the nest. The females soon return underground and start laying eggs. The workers transfer the eggs to another part of the nest in their mandibles and lick them clean. This licking also helps to maintain the correct humidity. The damp eggs stick together in batches which the workers carry into the nesting chambers where the blind, legless larvae will hatch out. The workers lick the larvae and transfer them from place to place, always depositing them where temperature and humidity are optimal. The larvae cannot find their own food and are entirely dependent on the care of workers. The workers feed them with either juices from their crops or secretions exuded from the labial glands. The larvae fed with these latter secretions pupate and hatch into sexual individuals. Those larvae fed only on the juices from the crop change into workers. When full-grown, the larva spins a silk cocoon in which it pupates. The cocoons of the future sexual individuals are always a little larger than those of the workers. The cocoons are often mistakenly called 'ant eggs'; this and several related species of ant are protected by law in some countries because these 'ant eggs' are much sought after by breeders of tropical fish and ornamental bird fanciers as food for their pets. As a result, many anthills have been destroyed.
Length ☿ 4—5 mm, ♀, ♂ 8—10 mm.

Family: Formicidae — Ants

⊙ ***Formica polyctena*** FÖRST. (continued). The care of the future generation by workers is unceasing: they clean the cocoons and transfer them to the most suitable places; later, they even help the young adults to emerge from the cocoons. After hatching the new workers are cleaned and fed for a period of about six days, then they are able to share in the activities of the anthill. The workers **(2)** not only feed the future inhabitants of the nest but also look after the queen, feed the males and each other. The exchange of food has certain rules. The food giver exudes a drop of liquid from her mouth which is eagerly accepted by another worker. She does not, however, retain the whole quantity for herself. As she was fed, so she in turn feeds another individual.

Males and females swarm in the spring. After the mating flight the females shed their wings, because they will not require them again. Each inseminated female — queen **(3)** has two tasks: to found a new nest (colony) and to lay eggs. In optimum conditions, the female enters a nest of its own species where there are already many other queens. Of course, her adoption by the others is not always successful. Many females are killed as the nest resists an influx of further queens. Thus, individual females only rarely found a new nest and then with the help of another ant species, usually *F. fusca*. The *F. fusca* queen is killed and the original workers used to bring up the *F. polyctena* offspring. The original inhabitants die out in time and the *F. fusca* nest changes into a pure *polyctena* colony.

F. polyctena often creates a number of large nests within a fairly small area. They originate by branching out from a nest where living conditions have ceased to be optimum. A group of workers leaves the original anthill, finds a suitable place in the near neighbourhood and lays the foundations of a new nest. The workers then return to the old nest for more workers, queens, larvae and pupae and carry them *en masse* into the new nest. The splinter groups and the original anthills are then connected by trails for a variable period of time.

This ant feeds on insects and sweet juices. Among its insect food are several wood pests but also some beneficial species — ichneumons, braconids, etc. A larger number of workers always share the pray **(1)**.

Compared with *F. rufa*, *F. polyctena* is more aggressive and predatory and so more appreciated by foresters. A large anthill consumes an enormous amount of food. *F. polyctena* is introduced into woods as part of biological pest control. Under expert supervision a part of a large anthill is transferred with its workers and several dozen queens to ensure the growth of the artificially created colony.

F. polyctena occurs in central Europe and temperate Asia. Like several other ant species, it is protected by law in a number of countries.

2 ♀

3 ♀

Family: Formicidae — Ants

⊗ **Formica rufa** L. resembles in size and coloration several other species but is most often mistaken for *F. polyctena*. It builds an underground nest and over it constructs a large anthill made from both coarse and fine materials. The average height of the nest is about 50 or more centimetres, while the circumference measures several metres (4). The nests are mainly monogynous; polygynous nests are rarely found. This ant is common in coniferous (spruce) and oak woods, especially in the lowlands and mountain foothills. It often lives in damp and shady habitats. The number of inhabitants in a nest can be estimated only roughly. A medium-sized polygynous nest contains about half a million ants. A large nest has about a million inhabitants, often more.

The males (3) and females (1) swarm from May onwards. During the mating flight the female is inseminated; she then sheds her wings and her next duty is to found a new colony. Many females die prematurely, becoming the prey of predatory insects and birds. The female is unable to look after the nourishment of the larvae and so needs workers from the very beginning. She is helped in founding the colony by workers of her own (2) or a different species. The most simple way for the female is to enter a nest of her own species and be accepted there. The situation is more complicated if she chooses an anthill belonging to another species, most often *F. fusca*. If there is no queen in it, the female enters the nest and is more or less easily accepted. Most anthills, however, already have a resident queen. In this case a fight takes place and the bigger and stronger intruder kills the native queen, settles down in her place and starts laying eggs. The workers — the original inhabitants of the nest — bring up their own offspring and that of the new queen at the same time. Gradually the original inhabitants die out, until in the end the anthill changes into a pure *rufa* colony. Sometimes there are many nests in close proximity, all originating from the main nest. *F. rufa* feeds on insects, the sweet honeydew of scale insects and aphids, sweet fruit juices, tree sap and oily seeds. In hunting prey the workers use both the mandibles and the poison gland, which lies at the end of the abdomen. The effect of the poison is well known. It is a common misconception to say that a wood ant stings. What it really does is break the skin with its strong mandibles, move its abdomen rapidly forwards and let a secretion containing mainly formic acid flow into the wound.

Formica rufa and related *Formica* species are very important in forestry because they consume a vast quantity of pests. This is why they are protected by law in some countries and one is not allowed to collect their pupae. They are also artificially introduced into some localities.

F. rufa inhabits a large part of Europe from the Pyrenees to Norway and Sweden, Siberia, the Caucasus and North America.

Length ☿ 6—9 mm, ♀, ♂ up to 11 mm.

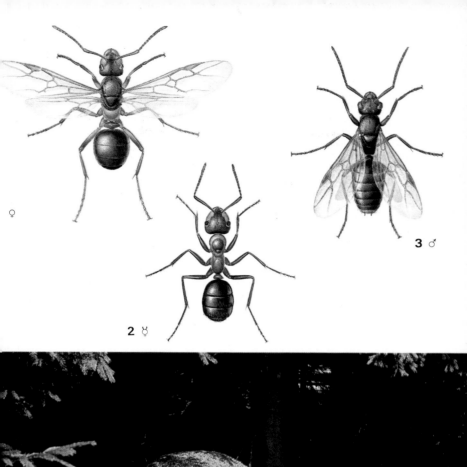

♀

2 ☿

3 ♂

4

Family: Formicidae — Ants

⊗ *Formica pratensis* RETZ. IN DEG. is very similar to *F. rufa* and *F. polyctena* but can be easily distinguished using a magnifying glass. The head, thorax and abdomen of the workers **(2)** are covered with long hair, while in both other related species the head is either entirely hairless or at least hairless at the rear.

F. pratensis lives in both lowland and hilly regions in open areas — hedgerows, meadows, ditches and sometimes in woods. It builds a combined nest. The upper part is not very tidy — it is usually a low, broad and flat pile which acquires a central hollow during the winter **(1)**. The ants build it from coarse materials (some from pine needles, in other places from various plant fragments or soil particles). An anthill of this species is densely populated but does not contain as many ants as that of *F. rufa*. The nest is monogynous or polygynous. The males and females of *F. pratensis* swarm mostly in the morning from June to September. New nests often originate by splitting off from the original one.

It is a beneficial species; its predatory habits can be observed in woods and fields. Pests predominate in its food: about a quarter are various species of no importance to man and only less than 10 per cent are species useful to man.

F. pratensis is widespread throughout Eurasia. In the Alps it reaches altitudes over 2,000 metres.
Length ☿ 4—9 mm, ♀ 9—11, ♂ 9—11 mm.

⊗ *Formica fusca* L. is covered with short hairs all over its body. It is one of the most common ants, living mainly in shady places on non-cultivated soils and also in gardens. The nest is built mostly underground, sometimes under stones but often also in old tree stumps **(5)** or under tree bark. If there are no stones in the locality, the ant builds little mounds.

It swarms from June to September. The mated female **(4)** founds a new colony independently, without the help of another ant species. She overwinters and starts laying eggs in the spring. The first workers appear about six weeks after egg-laying. Sometimes several females join together to found a nest. However, unlike other species, they do not start fighting when the first workers hatch. The nests of this species normally contain several queens (polygynous) and monogynous nests are rare. *Formica fusca* workers **(3)** live up to 8 years.

A tiny ant, *Solenopsis fugax* (LATR.), lives in *Formica fusca* nests or in their close proximity. It connects its nest to the neighbouring anthill by means of narrow tunnels. It steals the offspring of its neighbours and escapes with its prey through the narrow tunnels which are too small for the much larger *F. fusca* to enter. Even *F. fusca* is not entirely innocent of transgressions against its neighbours. It hunts not only smaller ants but also their larvae and pupae. It licks the honeydew exuded by aphids and scale insects.

The *F. fusca* nest often becomes subjugated by other ant species, which found their future nests with the help of the *F. fusca* workers. *F. fusca* brings up the offspring of *F. rufa*, *F. sanguinea* LATR., *Polyergus rufescens* and others. Its nest is regularly attacked and sacked by *Formica sanguinea* and *Polyergus rufescens* when obtaining new slaves.

F. fusca is widespread throughout Eurasia (in the Alps it reaches an altitude of 3,000 metres, while in southern Europe it occurs primarily in the mountains) and North America.
Length ☿ 4.4—7.5 mm, ♀ 7—10 mm, ♂ 7—11 mm.

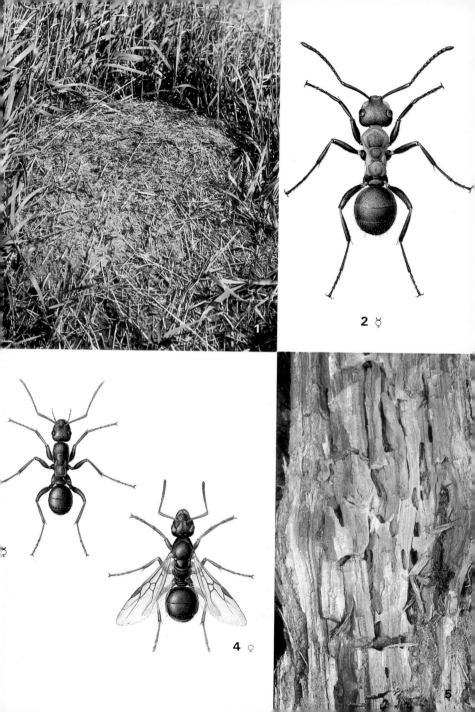

2 ☿

4 ♀

Family: Formicidae — Ants

⊙ *Camponotus ligniperdus* (LATR.) is very similar in both size and coloration to the following species. Both have a reddish-coloured thorax and petiole but *C. ligniperdus* has the basal part of the abdomen reddish to red-brown with sparse hairs. Two other related and similar species are entirely black. *C. ligniperdus* is very variable in colour and thus difficult to identify. Both this and the next species used to be considered as varieties of a single species and named *Camponotus herculeanus herculeanus* and *C. herculeanus ligniperdus*.

C. *ligniperdus* lives in woods but unlike the damp-loving, mountain-dwelling *C. herculeanus* it prefers open dry places in low-lying regions, especially the clearings in woods. Its nest is structurally identical to that of *C. herculeanus*. It mostly inhabits old tree stumps but also dead **(1)** and, less often, living trunks of conifers, mainly spruce, fir and pine. The nest contains, in addition to the usual-sized workers, conspicuously large individuals with large heads — 'soldiers'. The mating flight takes place in the early afternoon in the first week of June. The plump female **(3)** sheds her wings **(2)** after the mating flight; she then founds a new nest by herself, without the help of another ant species.

C. *ligniperdus* is widespread mainly in central and southern Europe, Asia and North America. It is a long-lived species; the workers **(4)** may reach an age of 13 years.
Length ⚥ 7—14 mm, ♀ up to 18 mm, ♂ 9—12 mm.

⊗ *Camponotus herculeanus* (L.), along with several related species, is one of the largest of European ants. It is very similar to the above species and its identification from only one specimen can be a problem even for the expert. The thorax and petiole are red, the whole abdomen is matt black and covered in thick hair **(5)**.

It is a typical woodland species. It occurs predominantly in damp places in woods, often in living trees (usually spruce), sometimes in the earth under stones. The nests of this and related species are quite different from the nests of other ants. Typically, the nest consists of a system of chambers and tunnels excavated in the wood of a tree trunk. The tunnels usually run alongside the annual rings in the centre of the trunk.

The males and females of *C. herculeanus* swarm in the late afternoon in early June. After the mating flight the female sheds her wings. She founds the new nest by herself, without the help of another ant species. She makes a chamber where she encloses herself and lays eggs. The eggs serve as food both for her and for the first larvae. The hatched workers **(5)** chew their way out of the chamber and gradually the new colony begins to function. The penetration of the ants into living wood damages the host tree. It attracts further damage by woodpeckers which chip off wood with their strong, sharp beaks in an attempt to reach their favourite food, the ants. An affected tree can be identified by the wood splinters around its base and by the holes made by the birds. The tree becomes fragile and snaps easily in strong winds. *C. herculeanus* is predominantly a mountain species, common everywhere at higher altitudes. It has been known to infest wooden buildings, the foundations of which it enters from the ground.

It is widespread in central and northern Europe, northern Asia and North America.
Length ⚥ 7—14 mm, ♀ up to 18 mm, ♂ 9—12 mm.

1

2 ♀

3 ♀

4 ☿

5 ☿

Family: Myrmicidae — Ants

⊙ **Manica rubida** (LATR.), in earlier literature known as *Myrmica rubida,* is covered all over its body with long upright hairs. It is one of the larger European ant species. It lives mostly in mountain regions, on sunny, dry, stony slopes with low vegetation, in pastures and in alpine meadows.

The nest connects with the outside by means of corridors with small entrances surrounded by mounds of earth. The nest contains about 1,000 workers (1) and usually more than one queen. This species swarms from spring to September. The female sheds her wings after the mating flight, constructs an underground chamber and encloses herself in it. She founds the nest by herself, without the help of another ant species. The larvae hatch about 4 weeks after the eggs are laid.

M. rubida has a sting connected with a poison gland. It uses it against even larger ants and the poisonous secretion kills them in a short time. This ant does not sting as rapidly as, for example, the wasp — it takes about 30 seconds.

It is widespread in southern and central Europe (in the Alps it reaches an altitude of 2,400 metres), Siberia and Asia Minor. It is not found in northern Europe and Great Britain.
Length ☿ 5—8 mm, ♀ 9.5—13 mm, ♂ 8—10 mm.

⊗ **Myrmica rubra** (L.) is one of the yellow to reddish-brown, medium-sized ants. Its identification requires, as with most European ants, a strong magnifying glass. As in related species, the females **(3)** and workers **(2,4)** are equipped with a sting; their sting is very painful and the wound continues to hurt for quite a long time. Apart from needing a certain degree of humidity, this species is not very demanding as to its choice of habitat. It occurs in woods and alongside woodland paths, in meadows, fields and gardens in both lowlands and mountainous regions. *M. rubra* builds its nest in the ground under stones, in tufts of grass, in moss or else makes a small mound. It often nests in rotting tree stumps, under bark and in hollow trees. It feeds mostly on vegetable matter, including nectar, and collects the honeydew of aphids; it also licks seeping plant juices, gathers seeds and has a penchant for strawberries. If there is a food shortage, it eats insects. The nest is either monogynous or polygynous. The winged individuals — males and females — are found as early as June.

The mating flight takes place between July and August. The mated female loses her wings and founds a new colony without the help of another ant species.

The distribution of this ant covers the greater part of Europe and temperate Asia and Japan; in southern Europe it lives mostly in mountainous regions and in the north extends as far as Lapland.
Length ☿ 4—5 mm, ♀ 4.5—6 mm, ♂ 4.5—5 mm.

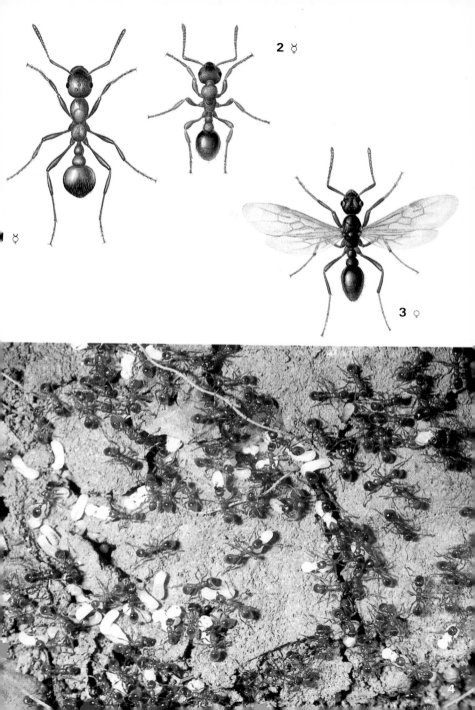

2 ☿

☿

3 ♀

4

Family: Myrmicidae — Ants

⊗ **Tetramorium caespitum** (L.) is very undemanding as to its nest site. It usually founds its nest in sun-warmed places with sparse vegetation. It occurs in a wide range of habitats, e.g. damp fields and gardens, various types of woods (mixed, beech, etc.) and even in mountainous regions.

Its nest is very variable. In most cases it is underground, often under a stone, but it may have a small earthen mound built over it. The anthill connects to the outside by tiny openings. *T. caespitum* also settles in rotting tree trunks and cracks in house walls. It feeds on various insects and eats the sweet honeydew of aphids.

It is quick and fearless and often wages war. Males and females swarm mainly in July and August but sometimes as early as May or June. After the mating flight the female sheds her wings; she founds the new nest by herself, without the help of another species.

T. caespitum **(1)** occurs throughout Europe, except for the far north. It is also widespread in North Africa, Siberia and Japan.

Length ☿ 3—4 mm, ♀ 6—8 mm, ♂ 5.5—7 mm.

⊗ **Monomorium pharaonis** (L.) betrays its membership of the family Myrmicidae by the two-segmented petiole connecting the thorax and abdomen.

M. pharaonis is one of the few ant species introduced by man throughout the world by means of trade and transport. In central European climatic conditions it is not able to live freely out of doors, because it would not survive the harsh winter, but is a regular inhabitant of centrally heated houses, greenhouses, swimming pools and hospitals. In such places it is considered a particularly troublesome pest, especially as it is thought to spread bacteria. It is omnivorous, occurring in large numbers on all kinds of foodstuffs. Its nest is rather primitive. It is always concealed, often in a crack in a wall or under the floor. Individual nests are often sited near each other. The nesting chambers are interconnected by long, narrow trails. A number of queens live in one nest **(3, 4)**. The winged males and females appear in September and October.

M. pharaonis builds many secondary nests; thus large numbers of ants may be present in any one locality. The individual workers **(2, 4)** would escape attention because of their minute size and light coloration, were it not for the fact that they are gregarious. They move rapidly along their paths, which are marked with a special secretion from abdominal glands, and hence find their way very easily with the help of their sense of smell. In view of the large number of nests, usually well concealed, the eradication of this ant is very difficult.

The home of *M. pharaonis* is probably in southern Asia (India). Its present distribution is cosmopolitan; it has settled in all tropical and sub-tropical regions and become more or less synanthropic in the temperate zone.

Length ☿ 2—2.5 mm, ♀ 3.5—5 mm, ♂ 2.8—3 mm.

1 ☿   2 ☿   3 ♀

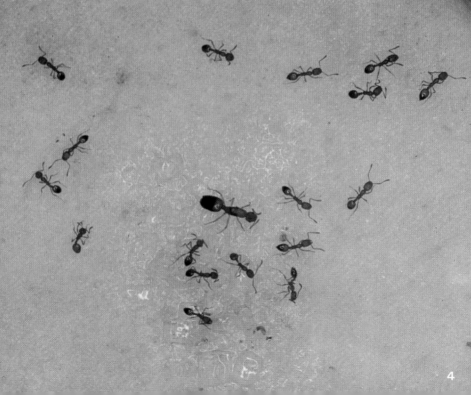

4

Insects in Ants' Nests

Anthills are shared by dozens of other insect species. They can be friendly, indifferent or hostile to their hosts. The following are several examples of beetles frequently found in anthills.

Family: Staphylinidae

⊗ *Dinarda dentata* (Grav.) lives in the nests of large ants of the genus *Formica*. Several beetles usually live in a colony at the same time. The overall appearance of *D. dentata* **(1)** is influenced by the ant species with which it is cohabiting. Thus there are several forms within the species. The beetle is well equipped for life in the anthill: its body surface is very smooth and hence the ants cannot grip it in their mandibles. It feeds on various debris and tiny arthropods.
Length 3—3.5 mm.

Family: Clavigeridae

⊗ *Claviger testaceus* Preyssl. **(2)** was discovered almost 200 years ago in the neighbourhood of Prague. It is a typical symphile; the ants rear it as a 'domestic animal'. It cohabits with ants of the *Lasius* genus, most often with *L. flavus*. Its blindness and underdeveloped mouthparts make it impossible for *Claviger testaceus* to live freely outside the nest and so it is confined to the anthill for the whole of its life. It exudes secretions from special glands at the apex of its wing cases (elytra) which the ants like to lick. The ants look after their lodger well and at times of danger carry it underground in their mandibles.   Length 2—2.3 mm.

Family: Monotomidae

⊗ *Monotoma conicicollis* Aub. **(3)** is common in the nests of large ants of the *Formica* genus, e.g. *F. rufa*, *F. pratensis* and *F. polyctena*. Its coloration and body shape mimic the building material of the anthill perfectly. It is probably hostile to its hosts.   Length 2.5—3.2 mm.

Family: Scarabaeidae

⊗ *Potosia cuprea* (F.) **(4)** sometimes develops in the anthills of *Formica rufa* and related species. Its whitish, fat larva feeds on vegetable tissue and is quite harmless to the ants. Wild boar, foxes and badgers damage anthills in their quest for this larva. The larva constructs a cocoon within the anthill and pupates in it; development takes two years.   Length 14—23 mm.

Family: Chrysomelidae

⊗ *Clytra quadripunctata* (L.) develops in anthills. The female has a very characteristic way of laying her eggs. She holds the egg with her hind legs and exudes a layer of secretion over it; when this solidifies, the whole structure looks like a seed. The ants pick it up and carry it into the anthill, where the larva hatches out; it glues together a tube round its body for safety and never leaves it. It feeds on ant larvae, eggs and pupae. The presence of these larvae in the anthill can considerably influence the numbers of ants in the nest. The grown larva pupates in its protective tube near the top of the anthill. The adult **(5)** hatches in the spring, leaves the anthill and lives on bushes in the vicinity.
Length 7—11 mm.

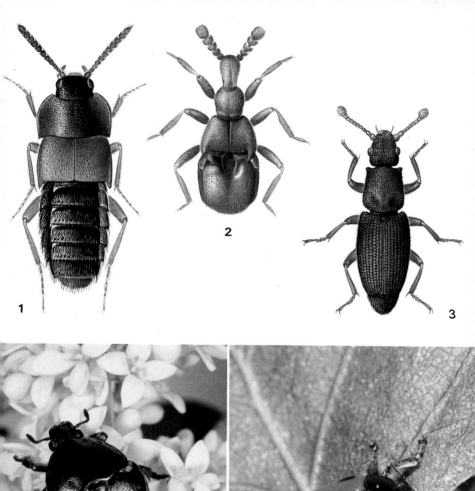

1

2

3

4

5

Family: Vespidae — Potter Wasps and Social Wasps

⊙ **Eumenes pomiformis** F. (1) is similar to the somewhat larger *E. subpomiformis*, with which it is often confused, and to other eumenid species. The larval development takes place in a very neat little 'pot', a structure reminiscent of a Greek amphora, constructed by the female (2). It is almost spherical, about 10—12 mm in diameter, thin-walled and coarse-grained on the outside. At the top it narrows into a mouth surrounded by a kind of collar. It is glued together with saliva and made from soil particles which the female transports between her mandibles and forelegs to the chosen site. She fixes the pot to the stem of a plant, a branch of a bush, a stone, a rock or a wall. Then the wasp inserts the end of her abdomen into the pot and suspends an egg from its ceiling. After doing it, she fills the pot with sufficient caterpillars for the future larva to feed on. Last of all she seals the pot with a thin layer of earth. The carnivorous wasp larva does not leave the pot during its life; eventually it pupates within it.

The pot is a solid structure but sometimes a parasitic insect species (often Chrysidoidea) manages to insert an egg into it. Their larvae find enough food inside, develop, pupate and instead of a wasp a chrysidid emerges from the pot.

E. pomiformis is widespread over most of Europe (except the north) and North Africa.

Length ♀ 11—17 mm, ♂ 8—12 mm.

⊙ **Symmorphus murarius** (L.) — Wall Mason Wasp — is very similar to other species of wasps (3). They all build nesting chambers and place in them the paralysed larvae of leaf beetles (Chrysomelidae). The nest are usually found in cracks in walls and often also contain Chrysididae, especially *Chrysis ignita* and *C. nitidula*.

This eumenid lives in central and southern Europe.

Length ♀ 11—17 mm, ♂ 8—12 mm.

⊗ **Ancistrocerus parietum** (L.) (4) is a more common species. It can easily be mistaken for several other species which at first glance are very similar; its correct identification requires a strong magnifying glass. There are two generations a year. The first one flies in the spring, the second from mid-August. The larvae of the latter generation overwinter in their natal nests. *A. parietum* nests are concealed, often in tunnels created by other insects. The larvae feed mainly on the caterpillars of smaller Lepidoptera but sometimes on tiny chrysomelids. The imagines frequent the flowers of Umbelliferae but are also found on thistles, yarrow, etc.

A. parietum is widespread over most of Eurasia (in Fennoscandia it reaches the far north) and North America.

Length 10—13 mm.

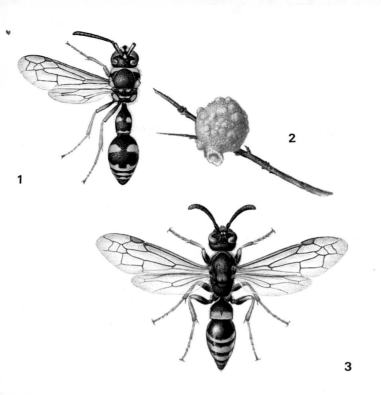

1

2

3

4

Identification of Wasp Nests

The nests of both the highly social wasps and *Polistes* species can be identified even without their inhabitants in residence. In the following key each criterion has an opposing one. For identification we need to read both parts of the couplet (e.g. 1 (2) and 2 (1)) which complement each other. We then decide which half of the couplet is most appropriate and then we move to the next number, until we eventually reach the name of the wasp which had built the nest.

Key

1 (2)   Protective envelope round the comb is absent. The whole nest consists of one comb fixed to one or more stems. The comb often hangs vertically or in a slanted position.

    a (d) The comb cells are roughly the same length, do not widen and lie almost parallel in the comb. The nest contains a relatively large number of cells (up to several hundred).

    b (c) The nest is light grey, fragile and usually built in a sunny position. In most cases it is fixed close to the ground on a plant stem, a rock, house wall etc. . . . . *Polistes nimpha* ⊙

    c (b) The dark grey nest is usually built on a site protected from the wind — in a well-lit hollow, under the eaves, etc. Often there are several nests close together . . . . *Polistes gallicus* **(1)** ⊗

    d (a) The cells of the comb are of uneven lengths and are arranged in concentric rays. The nest has a smaller number of cells.

    e (f) The nest is dark grey. The lid covering the grown larva in its cell is dark and lies under the cell edge. The inner cells of the comb are higher than the outer ones. The nest is usually attached to a rock, a stone etc. . . . . *Polistes biglumis bimaculatus* ⊙

    f (e) The nest is light-coloured, with yellowish overtones. The cell lids are whitish . . . . *Polistes foederatus* ⊙

2 (1)   A protective envelope of varying thickness and colour covers the whole nest, always containing more than one comb. The combs lie horizontally on top of each other and are connected by vertical struts. The nests are subterranean or above ground.

3 (8)   The nest is usually built in a well-lit place — on tree branches, bushes, loft beams, wooden roofs, window ledges, rarely on the ground or in a shallow depression (in the latter case part of the protective envelope will be visible). Individual combs are raised at the edges; the caps covering the larvae are very convex.

4 (7)   The nest is approximately lemon-shaped or spherical.

5 (6)   The entry opening is often provided with an extension. The protective envelope is pale yellow or greyish, resembling parchment. The nest contains about 300—500 cells and is mostly built on bush branches. It dies out in late August . . . . *Dolichovespula media* ⊗

Identification of Wasp Nests (continued)

6 (5)   The entry hole is without an extension.The protective envelope is grey to greyish-yellow. There are several hundred cells in the nest. It is built most often under eaves, in bird boxes, in treetops or partly underground (with part of the nest showing). It dies out in late August . . . .
. . . . *Dolichovespula sylvestris* ⊗
(The nest is often similar to that of *D. saxonica* and cannot always be identified without the wasps being present.)

7 (4)   The nest is strawberry-shaped or pear-shaped, with a broad top and narrowing towards the bottom, and grey in colour.
  a (b) The nest is hung most often under the eaves, in barns, lofts, tops of windows, haylofts, less often on trees. It dies out during August . .
  . . . . *Dolichovespula saxonica* ☉
  (see pict. **2** on p. 125)
  b (a) The nest is most often hung in dense, low shrubs (with leaves and twigs built into the protective envelope), in meadow hollows, only rarely under house eaves. It dies out during August . . . .
  . . . . *Dolichovespula norwegica* ⊗
  (The nest is often similar to that of *D. saxonica* and is difficult to identify without the wasps being present.)

8 (3)   The nest is built in a dark cavity, usually underground, in a hollow tree, in wall cavities, in house lofts, on verandas, in bird boxes, etc. Individual combs are straight, not raised at the edges. The cells are angular and straight-sided. The larvae are enclosed by only slightly raised caps.

9 (10) The sturdy nest is covered with a whitish-yellow to ochre multilayered envelope with longitudinal tubular-shaped sculpturing.The nest is cut off horizontally at the bottom to form a very wide entrance hole. It hangs most often in hollow trees, in corners of buildings or on beams in dark lofts . . . . Hornet — *Vespa crabro* ⊗
  (see pict. **3** on p. 125)

10 (9) The sculpture of the protective envelope is not tubular but scalloped. The entrance opening is small, the nest is not horizontal at the bottom edge or wide open.

11 (12) The protective envelope and the combs are yellowish or yellow-brown in colour. The nest has 8—10 combs and is always in a dark place, most often in the ground, in a hollow tree, a bird box, etc. It dies out in October
  . . . . The Common Wasp — *Vespula vulgaris* ⊗ **(3)**

12 (11) The protective envelope and the combs are grey.

13 (14) The nest is relatively small, mostly with only 3—4 combs. It is sometimes built in a shallow indentation in the ground suspended from grass roots, but more usually in a hole underground, close to the surface with a short approach tunnel leading to it. Sometimes it is built in a hollow log, a tree stump, etc. The nest dies out in late August or early September . . . . . .
  . . . . The Red Wasp — *Vespula rufa* ⊗ **(2)**

14 (13) The nest is relatively large, has 7—8 combs covered with a protective envelope with scalloped sculpturing. It lies relatively deep in the ground and is approached by a long tunnel. Sometimes it is built in a hollow brick, a bird box or a deserted beehive. It dies out in late October . . . . .
  . . . . The German Wasp — *Vespula germanica* ⊗ **(1)**

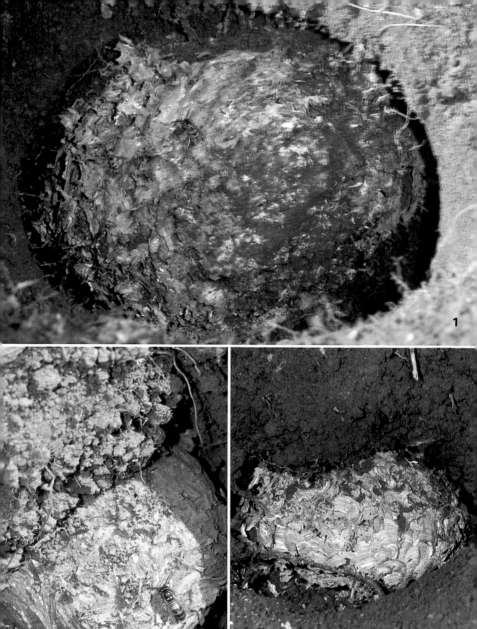

Family: Vespidae

⊗ *Vespa crabro* L. — Hornet — is the largest and most robust European social wasp. In central Europe it occurs in two colour forms, which are easily distinguished. In *V. crabro crabro* **(3)** the dorsal mesothorax is dark-coloured, while in *V. crabro germana* **(4)** it has a V-shaped red tracing.

The Hornet prefers to nest in oak woods and water meadows but also in large old parks. Often it occurs near human habitation but is not troublesome to man. The queen overwinters under the bark of a half-rotten tree stump or in old wood and then usually founds her nest in the same place or nearby. Hornets may nest in the same location for several successive years but never use the previous year's nest. Having selected a suitable place, the queen begins to build the nest foundations. The building material is old, powdering, rotten wood, mostly from old oaks and hardwood beams. This is why the nest is pale ochre-coloured. The hornet chews the wood with her mandibles, mixes it with saliva and carries it to the chosen place. First she glues together a stalk and then gradually adds several cells which form the base of the first comb. She begins also with building the protective envelope. She inserts a single egg into each cell. The hatched larvae hang in the cells with their heads down. At first they are glued to the cell by a sticky substance so that they do not fall out; as they gradually become fatter, they fill the whole cell tightly. The larva then closes the cell with a secreted silk cap and pupates. About 4—5 weeks after the egg-laying the first workers **(3)** hatch out and these relieve the queen of most of the duties which, until now, she has had to perform alone. They finish building the first comb; the building progresses very rapidly. A single worker can stick together a strip about 30 mm by 10 mm from a single 'collection' of wood material. As soon as the first comb is finished, the workers build another layer several centimetres below it. They attach it to the first one by a support made out of stronger material. To strengthen the nest further they add side supports to the main one. The same method is applied in the building of further levels **(2)**. Finally, they build a three- to four-layered protective envelope around the nest to keep out the elements and keep the nest dark **(1)**.

An average nest has about 5 combs but giant nests with up to 15 combs have also been recorded. The individual combs measure about 20 centimetres in diameter. The nest contains about 1,500 cells but the number of hatched individuals is much higher because the hornets reuse the cells. As soon as the adult hatches, the queen deposits a new egg inside the cell. As new combs are built, the top (original) combs become uncomfortable and more difficult to reach. The workers therefore sometimes wall them off with a paper-like partition or remove them. In the first combs all the cells are small. Both workers and males develop in them. Later on large cells are made which serve for the production of queens and further males. The protective covering of the nest has a beautiful, finely sculptured surface, faintly reminiscent of roof tiles. The nest has a wide opening at the bottom, as if it were cut off horizontally. This allows debris to fall out: hornets do not carry out their waste.

Length ⚥ 18—25 mm, ♀ 23—25 mm, ♂ 21—28 mm.

3 ☿

Family: Vespidae

⊗ **Vespa crabro** L. — Hornet (continued). The Hornet's nest is guarded at all times. A permanent guard is mounted by the entrance **(1)** and sounds the alarm in case of danger. This alarm calls the workers to prepare for immediate attack. The overwintered queens fly from mid-April to mid-June, workers from the beginning of July to mid-October, the males appear towards the end of September and the young queens during September. The emergence of the young females (the future queens) and the males heralds the end of the Hornet colony. After mating the males' sperm is stored in a special sac, the spermatheca, in the female's abdomen; a little is released each time an egg passes the entrance to the spermatheca and the egg is fertilized. The demise of the Hornet colony begins with a fall in the number of workers. Those still present in the nest neglect their feeding duties and the larvae lose weight and fall out of the cells. The Hornets then pick them up in their mandibles and throw them out of the nest. The queen dies, exhausted by all her egg-laying.

The Hornet is a predator. It hunts various insects, mainly Diptera. An analysis of hornets' prey revealed that it included up to 90 per cent flies. Hornets hunt their prey in sunny clearings, on dung heaps, compost heaps and on dead animals. They also gather nectar (e.g. from lime trees), suck the sap of injured deciduous trees and enter beehives where they feed on honey. Solid food, such as chewed-up insects, are carried back between the jaws, while liquid food is stored in the crop. They use only a part of the food for their own nourishment. In the nest they hand over the rest of the prey to the larvae, the queen and young individuals which are not able to hunt. The latter consume only a part of their share and pass on the rest to other hungry individuals. It could be said that here we witness a kind of communal stomach. The larvae take sweet juices as well as a gruel made of masticated insects or sweet substances of firm consistency. The hungry larvae can make their needs known by scratching the cell walls with their mandibles, so calling attention to themselves by a rasping vibration of the comb.

Hornets are only slightly influenced by the weather and make hunting trips and search for building materials on sunny or cloudy days, in wind or light rain. They also fly at night. However, a premature start to the cold weather is lethal to them. When the temperature falls below 15 °C for a long period in October, the workers can find little prey. The larvae (at this time also those of the future queens) then suffer from lack of food, lose weight and die.

Hornets are undoubtedly a very important component of our environment because of the large numbers of flies they kill in the neighbourhood of their nests. Moreover, they are a very beautiful species of Hymenoptera and magnificent builders of perfectly designed nests **(2)**. They do not directly attack man but are feared because of their size and 'wasp' coloration. I have approached their nest on several occasions, at times very close while taking colour photographs, and I was never attacked by the Hornets.

V. crabro inhabits a large part of Europe (not above 63° north) and Asia. It was introduced into the USA in the mid-19th century and spread to Canada in 1957.

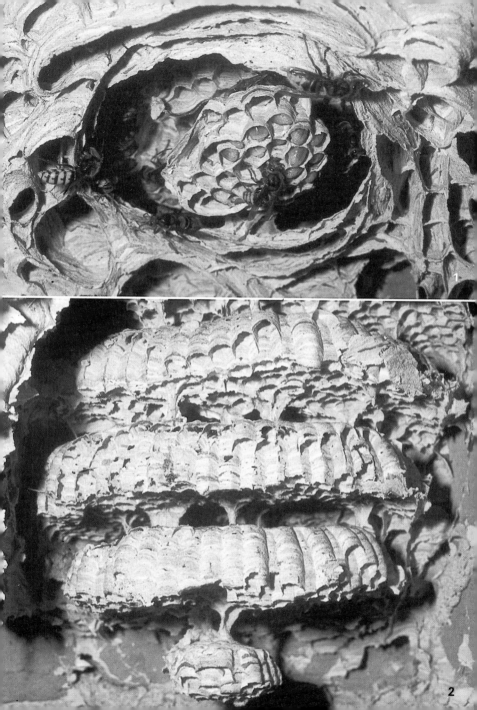

Family: Vespidae

⊗ **Vespula vulgaris** (L.) — Common Wasp — belongs, together with V. germanica, to the most common and best-known species of communaly living wasps. Both species are very similar at first glance. The workers can be distinguished best of all by the characteristic pattern on the clypeus. V. vulgaris has an elongated black mark widening ventrally **(1)**, while in V. germanica there are usually three separate black spots of various sizes **(2)**.

V. vulgaris nests underground, often in spruce woods, in meadows, grassy slopes, river banks, alongside roads, in gardens (even compost heaps), etc. Less often it nests in dark places above the ground, e.g. in hollow trees, in a wall cavity, or sometimes in a bird box. The site for the future nest is chosen by the queen after she emerges in the spring from hibernation. First she eats and then she surveys the terrain. She flies low above the ground and when she sees a hole leading underground, she lands. She carries out a reconnaissance of the underground cavity and if she is satisfied with her choice, she makes several short flights around the neighbourhood to fix the site of her future territory in her memory. Then she starts building the nest foundations. She constructs everything from a paper-like material she obtains from old, rotting wood. With her mandibles she scrapes off tiny fragments and mixes them with her saliva to make a small ball which she then carries off to the nest. There she works it further. First she builds the stalk, then several primary cells and the foundation of the future protective envelope. During the building she spreads out the paper-like material in a narrow strip. The cells are stuck together and hang with the open end downwards. As their numbers grow, a comb begins to form. The queen sticks a single egg inside each cell. The development of the new generation takes only 4—5 weeks, which is very important for the future survival of the colony. The queen would soon not be able to manage all the tasks required — at the beginning she not only has to build but also hunt prey and feed the first larvae. The first offspring — young workers (in fact sexually immature females — **3**) appear at the beginning of June and take over most of the queen's duties with the exception of egg-laying. Initially they continue to build the nest and feed the newly hatched offspring. They finish the first comb of cells and build further combs which lie parallel to the first and are interconnected by a stalk and side supports. They also rebuild and enlarge the protective nest envelope. With the growing numbers of inhabitants the nest cavity needs widening. This is also the workers' task. They carry tiny fragments of soil and stones out of the nest. Sometimes these fragments are much heavier than themselves. At times they encounter heavier stones or roots but they know what to do. Either they incorporate them in the nest, or, in the case of minor roots, they chew them off. The nest has to grow quickly in volume and numbers, since its lifespan is limited. The workers become more numerous and so the building work progresses faster. At the end of the season there are about 8—10 combs; the diameter of each is about 20 centimetres. The whole nest contains about 7,000 to 10,000 cells. Several thousand workers and several hundred males and females (queens — **4**) hatch out of them. The cell number, however, does not give the number of individuals hatched therein. Many of the cells are reused by the wasps. The first combs contain only small cells, the next both small and large cells. Workers and males develop in the small cells, while females and further males develop in the large ones. The greater the number of large cells, the older the nest is.

Length ☿ 11—14 mm, ♀ 16—19 mm, ♂ 13—17 mm.

1

2

3 ☿

4 ♀

Family: Vespidae

⊗ ***Vespula vulgaris*** (L.) — Common Wasp (continued). Let us consider the development of the Common Wasp. A larva hatches out of an egg. It is partly stuck to the cell so that it does not fall out. It is not capable of active movement and is entirely dependent on the care of the workers. The worker wasps feed it mostly with prepared juices they regurgitate from their crops. The older larvae can also take fragments of solid food. The larva moults its skin three times. In the last stage of its growth it is fat enough not to need sticking down as it fills the whole cell tightly. The full-grown larva makes a silky cap over the top of the cell, then spins a thin silk cocoon around itself and pupates inside it. The hatching wasp chews its way out through the cap and crawls out (2). It remains in the nest for some time before venturing out for its first reconnaisance flights. With the arrival of autumn young females begin to appear in the nest (at the beginning of September) and also males (from August onwards). The males are unable to help with the building of the nest or the feeding of the larvae. The workers, however, do not treat them as cruelly as in the case of bees: they do not kill them but allow them to live.

V. vulgaris workers cannot exist without their colony. They look after the nest building (1), the nesting space, the feeding of the young and, last but not least, the maintenance of a steady temperature (around 30 °C). When it is hot outside, the wasps vibrate their wings inside the nest and bring in water. They also use a secretion from the mouthparts of the larvae as a coolant.

The Common Wasp is a good, fast flier. Apart from level flight, it can also fly vertically, both up and down, and even backwards; its body axis remains in the same position throughout. In its search for food and building materials it is not much influenced by the day being clear or cloudy, by wind or by gentle rain. It is above all a predator. It hunts insects, preferably flies, which are its main food source. It does not hunt flying prey but attacks sitting or slowly moving individuals. It grips its prey in its feet, kills it with its mandibles and applies its sting if needed. It sucks out the prey's juices and converts its body into a kind of parcel — it bites off its legs, head and wings. It works very fast; in a few seconds or minutes (depending on the size of the prey) the 'parcel' is ready for transporting. Sometimes the wasp has difficulty in carrying it — it can weigh as much as four fifths of the wasp's own weight. The wasp also collects various sweet juices.

Towards the autumn the numbers of workers in the nest decrease, while those of males and females increase. This is the beginning of the end of the wasp colony. Because of the shortage of workers, larvae die of starvation; the cell becomes too large for them, they fall out on the roof of the comb below and the wasps carry them out in their mandibles. Only young fertilized females survive the winter. They crawl into sheds, cracks, house lofts, etc. and hibernate.

Many articles and books have been published on the importance of the Common Wasp and the German Wasp. Their positive contribution as predatory insects is well proven. Their negative activities must not be neglected either; all of us have felt the sharp pain of a wasp sting (only females and workers carry a sting — the male does not). The wasp, however, does not attack man, it stings only when its life or nest is in danger. Because it frequents unclean places, it may carry disease. Fruit growers dislike wasps in their orchards.

The Common Wasp occurs throughout Europe, temperate Asia, North America and Mexico. It has also been recorded in Australia and Hawaii (from 1960).

Family: Vespidae

⊗ ***Vespula germanica*** (F.) — German Wasp — is one of the most common wasp species in Europe. The queen **(1)** overwinters and in the spring founds a nest, often only about 20 centimetres underground in a dark cavity **(3** — nest entrance). The nests are most common in open spaces clear of vegetation, e.g. heaths, hedgerows, banks of streams, meadows, lawns and compost heaps in gardens. Less often the nests are found above the ground but in this case they are built in a dark cavity — sometimes in a hollow brick, at other times in a wall cavity, a bird box, a dovecote, a beehive or a pile of old rags in a garden shed.

The building material is old rotten wood of fences, telegraph poles or old dry timber. The wasp will also recycle old paper and old textiles. The protective envelope has a scallop shell pattern on the outside and the individual layers are tightly packed together. The inside of the envelope is smooth. The nest is grey in colour and so is easily distinguished from the yellowish-brown nest of the Common Wasp **(4)**.

There are usually 7—8 combs in the nest and each comb is about 20 centimetres in diameter. Most nests contain about 7,500 cells but considerably larger ones have been recorded. The cells are not of equal size. Some are smaller (those for the rearing of the future workers and some of the males); others are larger (the future queens and partly also the males develop in these). The top (older) combs contain only small cells because only workers **(2)** are produced at the beginning. From the fourth comb onward both small and large cells appear; large cells predominate in the last few combs. This mirrors the gradual increase in the numbers of males and young females. During the lifetime of the colony about 8,000 workers hatch in the nest; the males and females number several hundred. As in other species, the German Wasp reuses the cells.

The nest dies out in late autumn. The workers and males perish and only young mated females — the future queens — survive the winter. They overwinter in cracks, under tree bark, occasionally in the nest where they hatched. Sometimes several individuals overwinter together. The overwintering queen assumes a characteristic position: she grips the material under her with her mandibles and feet, tucks her antennae under her body and folds her wings longitudinally and presses them against the sides of her abdomen.

The queen flies out of her winter quarters as early as the second half of March. Queens appear in greater numbers during April and May. Workers are on the wing up to mid-November, males from mid-August to mid-November. Young queens appear from September to November. They do not have a mating flight like bees and ants but mate in the vicinity of the nest.

The German Wasp is a predator. The workers hunt insects, mainly flies, mosquitoes and various lepidopteran caterpillars. The composition of the prey of course depends on the wasps' habitat. They are also partial to sweet juices. They collect honeydew from the leaves of elms, oaks and aspens and suck nectar from flowers, visit fruits, fruit shops, sweetshops, larders and households, where they often end up running aimlessly up and down the window panes. Beekeepers dislike the German Wasp and destroy it near the hives as it also steals honey.

Its distribution is now worldwide, having been accidentally spread from Europe by man; in Europe it is absent only from the northernmost parts of Scandinavia and Finland.

Length ☿ 12—16 mm, ♀ 17—20 mm, ♂ 13—17 mm.

1 ♀

2 ☿

3

4

Family: Vespidae

⊗ **Vespula rufa** (L.) — Red Wasp — differs from other wasps mainly in the colour of its first and second abdominal segments which are orange-red. It slightly resembles the Norwegian Wasp which has lateral orange-red spots on the second and sometimes first abdominal segments. The Norwegian Wasp, however, has a long head; its cheeks are longer than half the width of the mandible at the base.

The Red Wasp is relatively common in quieter, open places in hilly regions; it also lives in gardens. It nests in the ground, sometimes in ditches, but the nest is well concealed so that not even a part of the protective envelope shows. It is usually built under the roots of grasses, trees, under timber, in old tree stumps, rotting logs, etc. The combs and the protective envelope are stuck together from particles of decaying wood scraped by the workers off wooden fences, telegraph poles, dry spruce trees, etc. This gives the nest its grey coloration (3); the nest of another ground-nesting species — the German Wasp — is very similar in appearance because both use identical building materials. V. rufa nests in holes in the ground near the surface and has only a short access tunnel leading to it. The entrance is usually hidden by vegetation. The nest is relatively small, usually consisting of only 3—4 combs containing several hundred cells. At first the combs only contain small cells in which workers and most of the males hatch. Later the workers begin to build larger cells (these can outnumber the small ones) which house all the females — the future queens — and a small number of males.

The lifespan of the Red Wasp is very short. The nest dies out some 4—6 weeks earlier than those of the German and Common Wasps. The queen (1, 2) overwinters, and emerges in the first warm days of spring, usually at the end of March, and starts to make the foundations of the nest. There she lays the eggs and rears the first workers. These then take over all the duties concerned with the construction of the nest and care of the offspring. The first workers emerge in mid-June, the last ones as late as towards mid-September. Young queens hatch out in August or September, males (4) from the beginning of August to mid-September. At this time the nest already starts to die out.

As all other wasps, it is a predator. It hunts especially for insect prey but can be commonly found on various flowering plants — willow, currant, raspberry, blueberry, various Umbelliferae, snowberry, etc. It also sucks nectar, gathers the honeydew of aphids and feeds on ripe fruit.

It is a non-aggressive species, indifferent to man's presence and rarely entering buildings. It is not attracted to either meat or sweet foods in households. The sting of the Red Wasp is described as less painful than that of, for example, the German Wasp. However, my own experiences do not confirm this. My 'intimate' acquaintance with both the German and Common Wasps during photography was rewarded by less painful stings than those of the Red Wasp. The Red Wasp stings were still painful three days later and, unlike those of other species, involved considerable swelling.

The Red Wasp is common throughout Europe, in the north reaching far into Fennoscandia (the Baltic shield); in southern Europe it lives in mountainous regions. It is widespread but not always common in the British Isles.

Length ⚨ 10—14 mm, ♀ 16—20 mm, ♂ 13—16 mm.

1 ♀

2 ♀

3

4 ♂

Family: Vespidae

⊙ **Dolichovespula saxonica** (F.) belongs to the long-headed wasps, together with its nearest relative *D. norwegica* (F.). This means that its cheeks are relatively long; their length (i.e. the distance between the mandible base and the lower edge of the compound eye) is considerably greater than half the width of the mandible. This feature, easily seen through a powerful magnifying glass, can help us differentiate *D. saxonica* and related species from the short-headed wasps like *Vespula germanica* and *V. vulgaris.*

Dolichovespula saxonica **(4)** is especially common in hilly wooded areas. It could almost be called a domestic species; among all the European wasps it is *D. saxonica* which nests most frequently in the immediate vicinity of man, even directly inside his dwellings. It is also common in the wild, wherever the nesting conditions are favourable. It likes daylight or semi-shade so that its nest is not built underground. While choosing a nesting site, the queen selects a place where the future nest will be protected from wind, rain and the heat of the sun. Her choice is not always a fortunate one, especially when the nest is clearly visible to man. She favours wooden ceilings and beams of chalets, forestry buildings, game mangers **(1)**, lofts of country houses, sheds or bird boxes of sufficient size (see illustration on p. 143). Sometimes the nest is built in a pile of timber or a tree, hanging from the underside of a thick branch. If the queen cannot find a suitable dwelling, she even makes do with a tuft of grass **(2)** where the nest is partly visible. I have observed a beautiful large nest in an asbestos pipe on a site where there were many other suitable nesting places, including a wooden barn and a house loft.

The nest is predominantly grey. The wasps stick it together from fragments of decaying wood. Later they also use the white silk caps the grown larvae use as lids to enclose themselves in their cells. These are visible in the otherwise grey material as whitish stripes. A finished nest is about the size of a child's head. It is usually shaped like a strawberry or an inverted pear, being attached by its wider part. The exit and entrance hole lies on the underside of the nest **(1, 3)**. There has to be sufficient space around it because the wasps fly into their nest at full speed. Picture 3 shows on the extreme right two wasps engaged in mutual feeding (trophallaxis).

It is very common to find several small nests, bereft of all life, hanging in close proximity from the beams in country lofts or newly built game mangers. Their builders — the queens — had either perished in inclement weather or fell victims to predators. These nests usually contain only a few cels or several combs. Length ☿ 11—14 mm, ♀ 15—18 mm, ♂ 13—15 mm.

Family: Vespidae

○ ***Dolichovespula saxonica*** (F.) (continued). The nest of *D. saxonica* contains 4 to 5 combs (see picture); the diameter of each is about 20 centimetres. The combs are slightly raised at the perimeter and the lids of the cells containing pupating larvae are rather convex. The average number of cells in a nest is around 1,300 (the maximum recorded is a little over 2,000). The cells are relatively large: their height is about 17 mm and their diameter about 4.5 to 9 mm. A protective envelope covers the entire nest with the exception of the entrance. The envelope is about 1 to 2 mm thick, strongest at the attachment stalk where it is composed of about 15 layers. The layers become less numerous towards the entrance, there usually being four to seven layers at the sides but only two to five around the entrance.

The colouring of *D. saxonica* is very variable. This applies to the design on the clypeus as well as the black pattern on the abdominal segments where the black coloration is sometimes replaced by yellow.

D. saxonica belongs to wasps with a short lifespan. The overwintered queens fly from the end of May, while the workers appear during July and young females and males mostly during August. The nest dies out as early as August.

Like other species, *D. saxonica* is a predator. It hunts various insects and likes to visit flowers where it sucks nectar. It is common on flowering snowberry bushes (pict. **4**, p. 141), where it is often in the company of other wasp species, e. g. *Vespula rufa,* and several bumblebee species. *Dolichovespula saxonica* also frequents flowering Umbelliferae; it can fly in cool wind and light rain.

Its activities are usually little influenced by climatic changes. Its flights after prey and suitable building material are undertaken even in a slight wind and during not very heavy rains.

It is a non-aggressive species and when it does sting, it is not especially painful. It is not only relatively harmless to man but is not a nuisance even in households. It does not attack man even when he moves in the immediate vicinity of the nests. I have had many opportunities to spend a number of hours near its nests when taking documentary photographs. The wasps did show a certain agitation and at the slightest provocation many of them rushed out of the nest. They ran around the protective envelope for a while but shortly crawled back in. Even the flash of the camera did not seem to disturb them unduly.

D. saxonica is beneficial to man because it destroys great numbers of flies and other pests. Therefore it is unwise to destroy its nests; on the contrary, safe nesting should be encouraged.

Another similar but parasitic wasp (*Dolichovespula adulterina* DU BUY.) lives in the nests of *D. saxonica*. It has no workers and so does not found its own nest but lets *D. saxonica* workers bring up its larvae.

D. saxonica is widespread through a large part of Europe but does not occur as far north as its relative the Norwegian Wasp. It is not found in the British Isles.

Family: Vespidae

⊗ *Dolichovespula media* (RETZ.) is a very variably coloured species even within the same nest. This wasp (1) prefers a well-lit location. It often builds its nest just above the ground — in a hedge, in shrubs, sometimes on rocks and higher trees. It does not inhabit bird boxes and enclosed underground cavities. It collects its building material mostly from live poplar trees. The nest envelope is parchment-like, yellowish-white or pale grey. The finished nest is lemon-shaped and often has a built-on extension facing downwards. The number of cells and hatched adults is low. Nests with some hundred cells are considered large in central Europe. The workers fly from the end of May and are still seen after mid-October; the young females appear in the first part of August. The males fly from just before mid-August to mid-September. *D. media* mainly hunts insects. Sometimes it appears on Umbelliferae and on snowberry, where it gathers nectar.

It inhabits most of Europe (in the north it occurs up to the Arctic Circle, in the south it is found in mountainous regions); it has recently been found in Britain, where it is rare.   Length ⚥ 15—19 mm, ♀ 18—22 mm, ♂ 15—19 mm.

⊗ *Dolichovespula sylvestris* (SCOP.) — Tree Wasp — lives in wooded hilly regions. It is not very demanding as to light or nesting site but does need high humidity. It prefers to build its nests just above the ground, mainly on trees, in bird boxes, empty beehives, barns, lofts and window recesses. If the nest is underground, it is at least partly visible (e.g. in a hollow between tree roots, etc.). The Tree Wasp gets its building material from fence posts or de-barked poplar trees. The nest is yellowish-grey and formed from several hundred cells. At the time of its demise (towards the end of August) there are about 250 females and about the same number of males. The overwintered queens fly from May, the workers from the end of May to September, young females in August and September, the males from mid-August to early September. *D. sylvestris* can often be found on flowers (2). It does not bother man and does not enter his homes.

D. sylvestris tends to be a warmth-loving species; it inhabits Europe (up to about 64° north) and North Africa.
Length ⚥ 13—15 mm, ♀ 15—19 mm, ♂ 14—16 mm.

⊗ *Dolichovespula norwegica* (F.) — Norwegian Wasp — lives in woods. The queen founds the nest in the place in which she overwintered or nearby. She is not demanding with regard to a nesting place, except that she requires high humidity and a sufficiency of light. The nest is built most often in dense shrubs, sometimes in a tree, rarely inside buildings or on the ground (in the latter case at least part of the covering is visible). The wasps acquire their building material mostly from healthy wood. They scrape it off with their mandibles from de-barked parts of living trees, fresh fence posts, etc. They incorporate twigs and leaves of bushes into the nest. The surface of the nest is patrolled by guards which give the alarm in case of danger. The nest usually has about 1,500 cells.

The colony is short-lived. The overwintered queens fly from the first third of May, the workers (3) in July and August and the males in the second half of July and early August. In August the nest dies out. The Norwegian Wasp hunts insects and sucks nectar from flowers, especially those of blueberry, snowberry, etc. It also likes to lick the honeydew of *Physokermes piceae.*

It is a common species, inhabiting a large part of Europe and temperate Asia.
Length ⚥ 11—14 mm, ♀ 15—18 mm, ♂ 13—15 mm.

144

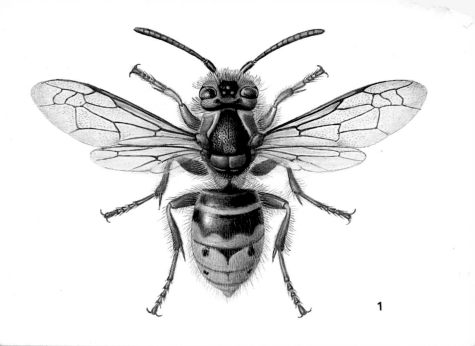

1

2   3 ☿

Family: Vespidae

The sub-family Polistinae has many features in common with the true wasps (Vespinae) but also shows many differences in both structure and manner of nest building. Like the Vespinae, the Polistinae also have the typical 'wasp' coloration — a very elegant combination of black and yellow. The females of both Vespinae and Polistinae have six and the males seven abdominal tergites visible from above. The females and workers in both groups have 12-segmented antennae and the males 13-segmented antennae. The males of both also lack a sting. The main differences between the two groups lie in the shape of the abdomen, the shape of the hind wing and the nest shape. While the abdomen in Vespinae is broad anteriorly, in Polistinae it tapers both anteriorly and posteriorly. Unlike the Vespinae, the Polistinae have a tiny, delicate lobe at the base of the hind wing. The social organization of the Polistinae is not as well developed as in the Vespinae and their nests differ a great deal in both size and structure.

⊙ **Polistes nimpha** (Christ.) flies from spring to autumn. The queen, which has hibernated, founds nest in the spring **(1)**. She builds the first few cells and rears the first workers. These and later other newly hatched workers continue to build the nest and feed the offspring. The nest is pale grey and fragile, constructed from fragments the wasps scrape off the bark of various shrubs. It consists of a single comb, containing only several dozen cells. All cells are the same length and placed parallel in the comb. The cell height equals approximately the length of the wasp's body. The nest has no protective envelope. The comb is attached by a short, thick stalk to a rock, stone, log, living or dead branch of a bush, plant or house wall. This stalk is the only support of the nest. Both the stalk and the nest surface are impregnated by an abdominal gland secretion which deters ants. The nest is usually placed only 10 to 20 centimetres above the ground as these wasps prefer high humidity. The further south, the better concealed the nest is. It often occurs inside houses or under the roof where it is protected from the heat of the sun.

P. nimpha is mostly predatory. It hunts various insects, which it macerates to feed its larvae. The adults also visit flowers where they suck nectar **(4)**. In the autumn they are attracted to over-ripe, rotting fruit. For many years I have observed them among strawberries in the garden. They arrived early in the morning to drink the dew from the leaves. Then they sat on the shed wall or a wooden tree stump and sunned themselves with their wings folded alongside their bodies **(3)**.

The workers and females of this species can be easily distinguished from the related and very similar Polistes gallicus by the black underside of their last abdominal segment; in P. gallicus it is yellow **(2)**.

P. nimpha is very common in parts of central and southern Europe and the southern part of northern Europe. It is not found in Great Britain, northern Fennoscandia or Denmark.
Length ☿ 14 mm, ♀ 16 mm, ♂ 12—15 mm.

Wasps' Cohabitees and Enemies

The nests of wasps attract a number of insect species which have various relationships with the wasps. Some are harmless to them, living only on the wasps' leftovers and making use of their shelter; others develop at the expense of the wasp larvae. The most frequently found orders are Coleoptera (beetles), Diptera (flies) and Hymenoptera.

Order: Coleoptera (Beetles)
Family: Staphylinidae

⊗ *Velleius dilatatus* (F.) develops mainly in the debris underneath Hornet nests in hollow trees, rarely under *Vespula germanica* nests. Both the beetle and its larvae hunt the larvae of various Diptera living in the debris beneath the nest. *Velleius dilatatus* also lays its eggs there. The larva builds a tube round itself. After the hornet colony dies out, the larvae burrow into the ground and overwinter. The beetle hatches in the summer of next year **(1).**   Length 15—24 mm.

Family: Rhipiphoridae

Metoecus paradoxus (L.) is known for its sexual dimorphism both in structure and colour. Its development is very complicated and took a full 130 years to clarify. The beetle **(2)** develops in the nests of several wasp species, mainly *Vespula vulgaris*. It emerges from the ground and remains in the neighbourhood of the nest. The female lays her eggs in decaying wood, which is the wasps' building material. From the very small eggs tiny (only about 0.5 mm long) larvae hatch; their legs are equipped with suckers. If a wasp lands on the wood they attach themselves to it and are transported to the wasp colony; otherwise they perish. The *Metoecus paradoxus* larva undergoes a very complicated development in the wasp's nest. It penetrates a cell where a wasp larva is developing and feeds on its body contents. Eventually it pupates in the wasp's cell.   Length 8—12 mm.

Order: Diptera
Family: Syrphidae

⊗ *Volucella zonaria* (Poda) as an imago lives on flowering plants but its larva develops in wasps' and Hornets' nests. The female enters the nest and lays elongated eggs on its paper envelope. The hatched larvae feed on dead wasps and vegetable debris. With the death of the colony they apparently supplement their food with the contents of the cells in the combs. The larva is about 20 mm long, whitish yellow, and covered in tiny warts which collect soil particles and so cover up their original colour. The grown larva pupates in the earth. The adults fly in the early summer of the next year **(3).**   Length 20 mm.

Order: Hymenoptera
Family: Ichneumonidae

⊗ *Sphecophaga vesparum* (Curt.) The larvae live in the underground and surface nests of various wasp species, which have been entered by the ichneumon female in the egg-laying period. The ichneumon larva feeds on the body contents of the wasp larva and eventually pupates in the cell. The afflicted cells are clearly recognizable by their rosy pink coloration **(4).** The cell is closed by a recessed lid which is translucent centrally. The lids of cells vacated by the ichneumons have a circular exit hole in the middle.   Length 8—9 mm.

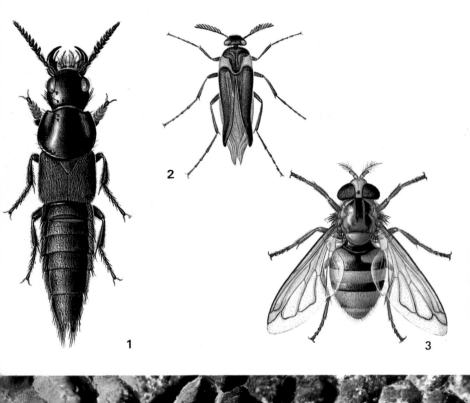

1

2

3

4

Family: Sphecidae — Solitary Wasps

⊗ *Ammophila sabulosa* (L.) — Red-banded Sand Wasp — is a warmth-loving species which prefers sandy sites. These sand wasps frequent the flowers of thyme, scabious, melilot, thistle, fireweed and various other plants from summer to late autumn in order to suck nectar (1). The reproduction of this and related species and their care of their offspring is very remarkable. The female (2) has a thick brush-like apparatus on her forelegs to enable her to excavate a nest for her larva. She selects a suitable site, digs the nest and masks the entrance. Then she sets out to hunt caterpillars, since the future larva is carnivorous and the female has to provide it with a sufficiency of food. When she manages to catch a smooth caterpillar (most often that of a moth), she paralyses it with several stings. The caterpillar remains alive but loses its ability to move. The sand wasp grips it in her mandibles, embraces it with her forelegs and carries it to the nest — often many metres away. She finds her way back easily (she locates the nest by sight, having memorized local landmarks). She places the caterpillar near the entrance and often spends some time arranging the nest. Eventually she crawls inside and drags the caterpillar in after her. She deposits an egg on one of the several caterpillars collected in this way, then fills in the tunnel and arranges the former entrance so that it is indistinguishable from the surrounding terrain.

The development is very rapid — in a few days the larva hatches and feeds on the paralysed caterpillar. It reaches full size in about 10 days, spins a cocoon and after a period pupates.

The Red-banded Sand Wasp occurs throughout the Palaearctic region. Length ♂ 16—23 mm, ♀ 20—28 mm.

⊗ *Podalonia hirsuta* (Scop.) — Hairy Sand Wasp (3,4) often referred to as *P. viatica*, flies from the end of April to October. It resembles the very common *Ammophila affinis*, from which it can be distinguished by the long hairs on its petiole. It inhabits warm localities. Like other sand wasps, it excavates its nest in dry sandy soils. The larvae feed on caterpillars, mainly those of moths. The female catches them, paralyses them with her sting and carries them into her nest cell where she lays an egg on one of them. The adult individuals are often attacked by parasitic stylopids (order Strepsiptera, genus *Xenos*). The stylopid sits between the abdominal segments of the wasp with part of its body protruding like a scale. In favourable localities this wasp is still common but it seems to be disappearing, like many other species whose life cycle depends on uncultivated land in warm regions.

The Hairy Sand Wasp inhabits a large part of the Palaearctic region. Length ♂ 14—19 mm, ♀ 16—23 mm.

⊗ *Crabro quadricinctus* F. resembles other species but can be distinguished mainly by the fine surface ridges on the thorax. It nests in old wood. The female (6) hunts flies — provisions for her future offspring. The imagines frequent flowering Umbelliferae (5).

C. quadricinctus occurs throughout Europe. Length ♂ 9—13.5 mm, ♀ 12—17 mm.

1 ♂

2 ♀

3

4

5

6 ♀

Family: Sphecidae — Solitary Wasps

⊗ ***Philanthus triangulum*** (F.) — Bee-killer Wasp — closely resembles several other species and could be mistaken for *Bembix rostrata* (L.). Its head, however, is broader than its thorax (the body shape viewed from above is club-like), the short antennae are widened in the middle, the clypeus is white and the eyes black. In *B. rostrata* both the eyes and the clypeus are greenish yellow. The imagines (1) live from June to September. The male sits on flowers, while the female is predatory and hunts honeybees. She paralyses the bee, embraces it tightly with her middle pair of legs and licks the honey-like substances leaking from the bee's mouthparts. She excavates a nest for her offspring, usually in warm, sandy locations with scant vegetation. The excavation is facilitated by her strong mandibles and modified forefeet which bear strong spines. The feet are used to throw the sand behind her during excavation. The nest (2) contains a main tunnel of variable length with branching side tunnels, each of which ends in a nest chamber. There are usually 5—7 chambers in the nest. The female inserts 2—3 paralysed bees into each chamber. She holds them parallel under her body during the journey to the nest. She lays an egg on one of the bees. The larva hatches in 3 days and feeds on the body contents of the paralysed bees. The grown larva overwinters in the chamber within a bottle-shaped cocoon and pupates in late spring. The adults hatch in July. *Philanthus triangulum* used to be considered harmful to bees but is no longer common.

It occurs throughout the Palaearctic region.

Length ♂ 8—10 mm, ♀ 13—17 mm.

⊙ ***Bembix rostrata*** (L.) appears in mid-summer. It is an excellent flier (3). The female hunts large flies, e.g. hoverflies, houseflies, horseflies etc. on flowering plants. She digs a shallow nest (about 15 centimetres deep) in fine sand with a level or slightly sloping surface. She feeds the larvae with paralysed flies and continues to provide supplies during the whole development period. A female can rear about 6 larvae. This species is also becoming rare as its habitats disappear.

It inhabits the whole of the Palaearctic region, except Britain.

Length 15—22 mm, fore-wing span 32 mm.

⊗ ***Cerceris arenaria*** (L.) — Sand-tailed Digger Wasp — belongs to the best-known species of this order in central Europe. It can be distinguished from other solitary wasps and wasps in general by the constrictions of its abdominal segments (5).

The adults fly from May to September and tend to be slow fliers. This wasp is warmth-loving and likes to sit on various flowers (4). The female digs her nest in sandy soils, often near young pine woods, where she hunts weevils. She paralyzes the beetles and stocks her nest with them. Sometimes she attempts to take over a nest made by another solitary wasp to avoid having to dig one of her own.

C. arenaria is widespread in Europe and north-west Africa.

Length ♂ 8—12 mm, ♀ 11—15 mm.

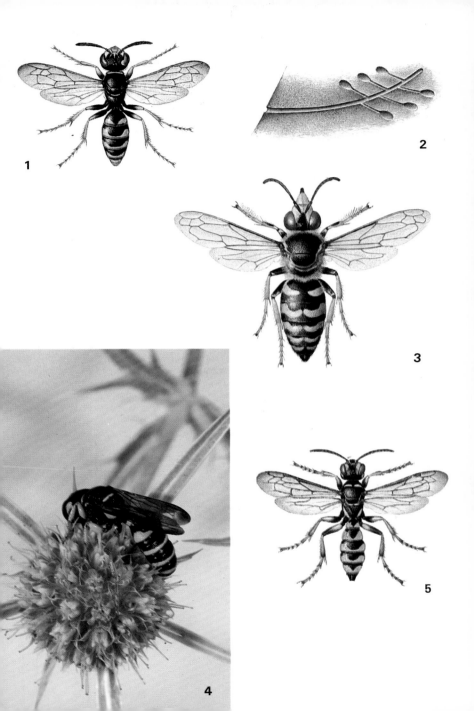

1

2

3

4

5

Family: Sphecidae — Solitary Wasps

⊗ **Mellinus arvensis** (L.) — Field Digger Wasp — is one of the most common solitary wasps in central Europe. The adults **(1, 2)** fly from late June to late October. Sometimes they can still be seen on fine November days. In certain places they are more numerous in autumn than in summer. This solitary wasp frequents animal droppings and sometimes human excreta, where it sits cleaning itself and hunting various species of Diptera. The female excavates a nest up to 75 centimetres deep; this extraordinary achievement is accomplished within a single day. The nest entrance is 6—7 mm wide. The female provides the larvae exclusively with various Diptera which she paralyses with her sting. She deposits more than 10 captured individuals in each cell and glues an egg onto one of them. Due to the character of the food provided, the development is rapid, as in other solitary wasps. The larva grows to full size in about 9—11 days and spins a cocoon in which it pupates.

The Field Digger Wasp is common in most of Europe.

Length ♂ 7—11 mm, ♀ 11—14 mm.

⊗ **Trypoxylon figulus** (L.) — Black Borer Wasp — is also a common solitary wasp species. It flies from late April to August. In contrast to many colourful, black and yellow species, this wasp is inconspicuous **(3)**. This species contains several biological forms. The experts believe this variation is due to the kind of nest and quality of food at the larva's disposal during its development.

The Black Borer nests in various situations. The female uses tunnels made by other insect species, e.g. solitary bees, in sandbanks or tunnels made by the larvae of various beetle and hymenopteran species in old wood. Using her mouthparts, she also makes her own nests by excavating tunnels in stems, especially those of blackberry. She is well adapted for this task in having a slim, elongated body and relatively short legs. She also nests in hollow reed stems in the thatch of country houses. After making or taking over a tunnel she subdivides it by partitions into separate chambers. Each of these she provides with a number of spiders. After capturing the spiders she paralyses them with her sting. There may be only a few spiders in the chamber but over 40 have been found. Their size is the decisive factor; the Black Borer female does not specialize in particular spider species. She inserts an egg into each chamber. The larva which soon hatches out has an ample supply of food all around it.

The Black Borer nest is often found and invaded by a chrysidid or ichneumon female. Then a parasite hatches out instead of the original inhabitant — the Black Borer Wasp — which has served as food to the parasite.

This solitary wasp occurs over most of the Palaearctic region.

Length ♂ 5—10 mm, ♀ 6—12 mm.

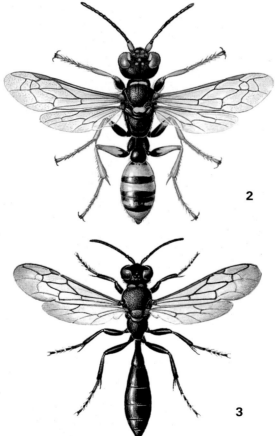

1

2

3

Family: Colletidae

⊗ **Colletes daviesanus** SM. — Davies's Colletes — typical of primitive solitary bees, has only a short tongue **(1)**. In most localities it is the most common of all European species. At the height of summer it can often be seen on the flowers of yarrow, tansy etc. It nests communally in steep banks. The female excavates a horizontal tunnel, about 10—15 centimetres long, leading to the nesting chamber which she lines with a transparent, silk-like secretion from a gland in the abdomen. The individual cells are tube-like and placed so that the ceiling of each cell is also the floor of the one above. There is a single generation each year. The larvae overwinter in their cells.

This bee is widespread in Europe and Siberia. Length 8—11 mm.

Family: Andrenidae — Mining Bees

⊗ **Andrena flavipes** PANZ. — Yellow-legged Mining Bee — is one of the common species of the extensive family Andrenidae (mining bees) which encompasses almost 200 species in central Europe alone. The adult **(2)** is covered with yellowish-brown hairs even on the edges of the abdominal segments. There are two generations a year. The first generation of bees are among the pollinators of the first spring flowers, as they fly from the end of March to May. The adults of the second generation fly in July and August and often frequent flowering Umbelliferae. It is a very numerous and useful species, being an important pollinator of fruit trees and other economically important plants, e.g. oleiferous plants and alfalfa. Like all other *Andrena* species, it is a solitary ground nester, in both clay and sandy soils; sometimes, many hundreds of females nest in a small area.

It inhabits almost all of Europe, Asia Minor, Central Asia and North Africa.
Length 11—13 mm.

⊗ **Panurgus calcaratus** (SCOP.) — Spurred Panurgus — is very numerous and, unlike many other solitary bees, relatively easy to identify **(3)**. The females have black tibiae covered with yellowish-brown gathering hairs and the males' hind femora carry a blunt projection. The larger females (10—12 mm) of *P. banksianus* (KIRBY) have brownish-red tibiae and rust-tinged pollen-gathering hairs; the males have no blunt projections on the hind femora. The latter species usually inhabits foothills. The imagines of *P. calcaratus* appear mainly in July and August and prefer the yellow flowers of hawkweed and dandelion. They either lie in these flowers or crawl among the individual florets; this is why their bodies become densely covered with pollen. They nest in the hardened earth of paths, often communally. Several females have been observed to use one entrance to a common nest.

P. calcaratus occurs throughout Europe. Length 8—9 mm.

⊗ **Andrena armata** GMEL. recently named *A. fulva* (MÜL IN ALL.), is a very strikingly coloured bee **(4)**. It flies in early spring, from mid-April to mid-May. It is an important pollinator of fruit trees, especially cherry and apple, in localities where there are few honeybees. To a certain extent this is a city bee. It frequents large parks and gardens where it likes to suck nectar from flowers **(5)**. Apart from fruit trees, it also seeks out hellebores, potentillas, maples, willows, etc. It nests in the ground. We can often see the entrance holes to the nests on clay paths in parks.

It occurs in central and north-west Europe and the Balkans.
Length 12 mm.

Family: Halictidae — Mining Bees

☉ *Halictus quadricinctus* (F.) is the largest central European species of this genus. Its abdomen bears four transverse bands of white hairs, sometimes interrupted in the middle. The nest of this solitary bee, like that of most of its close relatives, lasts only for a single season. The nest of *Halictus marginatus* BRULLÉ forms the exception — it lives for 5—6 years. The adults of *H. quadricinctus,* both males **(1)** and females **(2)**, fly in August and September and like to sit on the inflorescences of cornflowers. The males die in the autumn; only the fertilized females survive the winter. In the spring (May and June) the female frequents the flowers of hawkweed and scabious. Before starting to build the nest she surveys the terrain to ensure that the conditions are suitable. First she excavates a tunnel; as she works, she moistens the soil with glandular secretions. She obviously finds the moistened material easier to build with and the tunnel and cells she creates are strong and durable. The nesting cells are built from soil particles glued together. These cells are closely grouped together, resembling a bunch of grapes. The nest entrance hole is only just large enough for the bee to get through but the tunnel widens slightly further on. Both the grouping of the cells into a bunch and the overall architecture are characteristic of this species. Apart from a tiny support attaching the cell cluster to the walls, the bee removes the remaining soil from around the nest cells. This creates an air space around them which provides excellent insulation and protects the nest from mould. The female provides the nest cells with pollen — the larvae's food — and lays an egg in each cell. Because the cells open into the common tunnel, the bee has easy access to them at all times. She keeps the cells clean, looks after the larvae and brings them food. Eventually they pupate and at the end of summer the young bees hatch out. This species often nests close to other solitary bees.

H. quadricinctus occurs throughout the Palaearctic region, but is absent from the British Isles.
Length 15—16 mm.

⊗ *Lasioglossum albipes* (F.) shows marked differences between the sexes. Compared with the male **(3)**, the female looks like a small honeybee. The adults can often be seen on flowering plants, especially dandelions, from spring to autumn. This is a primitively social species.

L. albipes is widespread through a large part of the Palaearctic region.
Length ♂ 7—8.5 mm, ♀ 8.5—9 mm.

⊗ *Sphecodes monilicornis* (KIRBY) **(4)** is one of a whole range of similar species whose lifestyles are poorly understood. They are a black species with a red abdomen. The females have no pollen-gathering brushes on their legs.

The *S. monilicornis* female does not found her own nest but lays eggs in the nests of other halictid bees (e.g. *Lasioglossum* species). She enters the nest and lays an egg in an incomplete cell. The *Sphecodes* larva hatches first, eats the eggs of the host bee, then consumes its pollen provision. Females of varying sizes have been recorded; their size depends on the amount of food in the host's cells.

S. monilicornis occurs throughout Europe.
Length 7—10 mm.

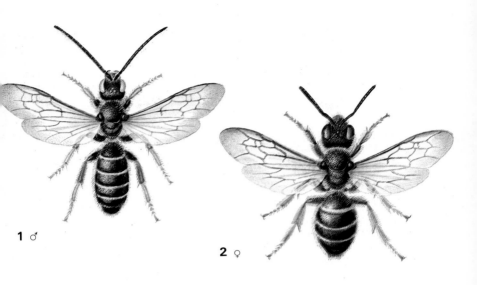

1 ♂

2 ♀

3 ♂

4

Family: Melittidae

⊗ **Melitta leporina** (Panz.) **(1)** is an important pollinator of alfalfa and clover and is numerous in the summer months (July, August). It also frequents the flowers of Common Melilot. The nest is a vertical tunnel in the ground, built by the female, with several cells projecting from it horizontally. The cells are lined with a waxy layer secreted by the female and provided with a supply of pollen for the larvae. After egg-laying the female walls off each cell with a clay lid.

    M. leporina inhabits a large part of Europe.   Length 11—13 mm.

⊗ **Dasypoda altercator** (Harr.) — Hairy-legged Mining Bee **(2)** — is also known as *D. plumipes*. The female has long, thick hair on her hind legs which serves for both gathering pollen and removing excavated sand from the nest. Due to these hairs, she can gather pollen easier and faster than other bees and so provide more food for her future offspring. The adults are numerous in July and August, especially on the flowers of hawkweed, chicory and other plants. *D. altercator* builds its nests in sandy banks. The female excavates a tunnel up to 60 centimetres long. She removes the loose sand from the nest by crawling backwards through the tunnel with the help of her middle pair of legs. She throws the sand away from the entrance by rapid movements of her forelegs and sweeps it away, using her hairy hind legs as brooms. Eventually there is a small furrow in front of the nest with ridges of sand piled up on each side. The tunnel branches into five or six horizontal shafts, each ending in a nest cell. *D. altercator* provides each cell with about 300 mg of pollen which represents about seven pollen-gathering expeditions. She forms the pollen into a ball and supports it by three tiny plinths made of sand; this allows the air to circulate freely under it and prevent its deterioration. She lays her egg on top of the pollen ball, then blocks up the cell entrance and eventually the whole entrance tunnel with sand. The larvae overwinter in the cells and pupate during the following year. There is only one generation in a year. In favourable localities *D. altercator* often nests communally, with several females sharing a common nest entrance.

    D. altercator occurs in a large part of the Palaearctic region.   Length 12—15 mm.

Family: Megachilidae

⊗ **Megachile maritima** (Kirby) — Coast Leaf-cutter **(3)** — can often be seen on thistles and cornflowers in July and August. The female builds a nest for her larvae in the sand under stones. The nest cells are lined with fragments of leaves which she 'cuts off' with her mandibles from several plant species.

    M. maritima, in spite of its name, occurs in central and northern Europe. Length 14—17 mm.

⊗ **Osmia rufa** (L.) — Red Osmia — is one of the most common solitary bees flying in early spring **(4)**. It frequents the flowering catkins of *Salix* species and also lungwort, sweet violets and other flowers. It also occurs in gardens, if it can find sufficient food (e.g. flowering hyacinths, crocuses, etc.). It nests in cavities in wood, cracks in walls, sturdy grass stems, etc. The female divides the space into individual cells with partitions made from soil particles moistened with saliva. She also colonizes the abandoned nests of other solitary bees. Her nests become prey for the parasitic larvae of *Chrysis ignita*.

    Osmia rufa lives in southern and central Europe and as far as the Caucasus. Length 8—13 mm.

1

2

3

4

Family: Anthophoridae

⊗ **Anthophora plumipes** (PALL.), also known as *A. acervorum* (L.), is covered in black or greyish-brown hairs **(1)** and has an exceptionally long tongue which equals the length of its body. It flies in late March and early April and pollinates lungwort, primroses, fumitories, etc. It excavates its nest in clay banks or old walls. The adults hibernate over winter in their natal cells.

    A. plumipes occurs throughout the Palaearctic region.   Length 14—16 mm.

⊗ **Eucera longicornis** (L.) — Long-horned Eucera — is the most common species in this genus. As in some of the related species, the antennae of the male are exceptionally long; in this species they are as long as the body. The adults **(2)** often occur in large numbers in May on vetches and oxtongue. The males appear before the females. *E. longicornis* nests in the ground. The nest takes the form of a vertical tunnel with the individual cells leading off it. The female provisions the cells with pollen and then lays an egg in each.

    E. longicornis is widespread over almost the whole of Europe.
Length 12—15 mm.

⊗ **Nomada sexfasciata** PANZ. **(3)** and many related species resemble wasps rather than bees. The female is unable to construct her own nest and provide it with pollen; therefore she invades the nests of other bees (mainly *Eucera* species) and lays her eggs in them. The whole development takes place at the expense of the offspring of the original inhabitant. She frequents the flowers of oxtongue in late spring (May and June).

    N. sexfasciata is widespread throughout the Palaearctic region.
Length 11—12 mm.

⊙ **Xylocopa violacea** (L.) is the largest and most robust of the central European solitary bees. It is a warmth-loving species, inhabiting grasslands and river valleys. It resembles the related *X. valga* **(4)**, which is more numerous in some habitats, in its coloration. The antennae of the male *X. violacea* are yellowish towards the apex. The adults **(5)** hatch in late August and in September. Both the males and females overwinter in hollow trees, walls, etc., often in groups. They mate in the spring. They fly from May to August and often frequent vetches, Viper's Bugloss etc. During her life, the female *X. violacea* builds one to three nests in old hollow trees, tree stumps and similar places. First she chews out a short horizontal entrance tunnel; then she excavates a vertical tunnel about 15 to 30 centimetres long, usually with an exit hole at the upper end. This hole is closed off with wood fragments. She divides the nest space into 10 to 15 cells. Each of these is about 20 mm long and 15 mm in diameter. These cells are separated by partitions made of wood pulp mixed with saliva. She deposits about 2 g of pollen in each cell as food for the future larva. A single larva develops in each cell. If the cell walls are thin, the emerging adult bites its way out through the side. However, if they are thick, it has to wait until the bees in the upper cells hatch out. Then the adults crawl out in succession through the exit hole. The young females found their own nests the following year, usually near where they were born. Because of this, *Xylocopa* is still common in localities unaffected by man but has disappeared elsewhere.

    X. violacea lives mainly in southern Europe and does not extend north of central Europe.   Length 20—23 mm.

1

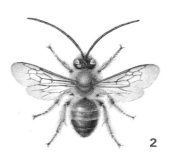

2

3

4 ♂

5

Family: Apidae — Honeybees and Bumblebees

⊗ *Apis mellifera* L. — Honeybee — also commonly referred to as *A. mellifica,* is regarded as a domestic animal in spite of never having become one. As early as 6,000 years ago it was kept by the ancient Egyptians. This is illustrated in many of their graves and temples. Although the bee has been domesticated to a certain extent, it is quite capable of existing independently of man. Man tries to direct its lifestyle by providing safe and comfortable nesting places (hives) with all the necessary building materials and supplementary food.

The European honeybee is found in several forms. The best known for its diligence is the Carinthian bee. The bee lives communally in a large colony of some 40,000 to 80,000 individuals. None of the colony are capable of existing independently of the rest. The colony is headed by the queen. The most numerous inhabitants are the workers (immature females); the males (drones) are only remporary members.

All three castes differ in both size and physical characters. The queen (1) is the largest and her abdomen is more elongate and slimmer than that of the workers. The drone (2) is robust, with noticeably large eyes and, unlike the queen and the workers, it has no sting. The queen and workers have a sting with little barbs, so that after it has been used the sting remains in the wound with some of the viscera and the bee perishes. The queen and the workers (3) are permanent residents of the colony. The males only appear in the spring and early summer. Each caste has its own strictly defined task. The queen lays eggs and so ensures the maintenance of the numbers in the colony. The workers build honeycombs, gather food, guard the nest and keep it clean, take care of the queen and the larvae, and at certain times also of the males. The males hatch in very large numbers, in spite of only a few of them being necessary for the survival of the colony by fertilizing the young queen. The males are chased out of the colony by the workers but because the males are unable to find their own food outside, they try to re-enter. However, the workers bite them and in the end sting them to death.

The bees build their nest from a material they themselves secrete: it is not a paper-like material as in wasps but a wax. The workers secrete it at certain periods of their lives from special glands on the abdomen. They scrape it off with their feet and knead it with their mandibles into a material from which they construct three types of cells. Regular hexagonal cells about 5 mm in diameter predominate; these serve for the rearing of workers. The second type of cell is slightly larger. These are intended for the development of the males. The entirely different bunch-shaped queen cells (both on the combs and on their edges) are destined for the production of future queens. Each comb consists of two layers (both layers are attached to each other by their bases) and the mouths of the individual cells are angled slightly upwards. This elevation is important since the cells not only serve for the rearing of larvae but also for the storing of provisions — pollen and honey. Wild bee colonies have to build the whole comb from the beginning by themselves. The hive bee is in a slightly better position; its work has been simplified by the beekeeper who inserts frames with vertical partitions into the beehive, each bearing a wax foundation. The workers then attach their hexagonal cells to these.

Length ♀ 12—15 mm, ♀ 16—20 mm, ♂ 14—18 mm.

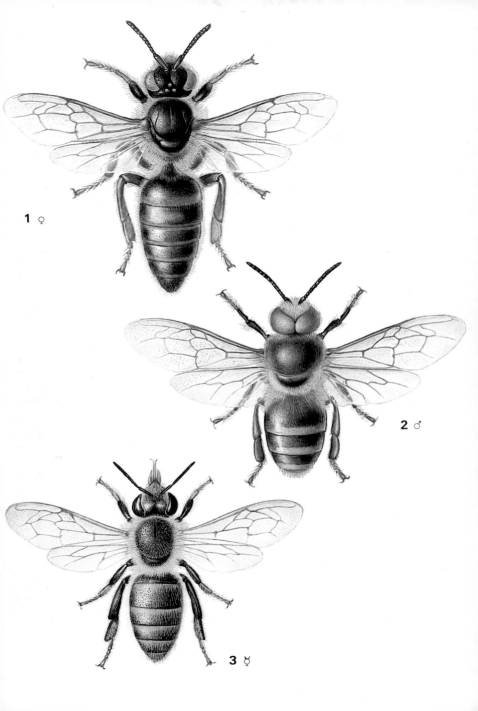

1 ♀

2 ♂

3 ☿

Family: Apidae — Honeybees and Bumlebees

⊗ *Apis mellifera* L. — Honeybee (continued). The development of the Honeybee is very rapid. The queen **(3)** lays a single egg inside each cell which has been cleaned and prepared by the workers. By building certain types of cells the workers predetermine what kind of eggs the queen lays in them. In the female's abdomen there is a special sac. After the mating flight the sac is filled with sperm which remain alive for several years. During the egg-laying the queen with the help of a complicated mechanism either fertilizes the eggs or lays them unfertilized. She lays fertilized eggs in the smaller cells (where workers will develop) and unfertilized eggs in the larger cells (where males will develop). After only four days a tiny larva hatches out of the egg and grows rapidly. It cannot find its own food and is entirely dependent on the care of the workers. It is fully grown in another five days, its weight having increased about 500 times. The full-grown larva fills the whole cell and the workers then close the cell with a wax cap. The larva spins a silk cocoon around itself inside the cell. The cell caps differ; we can determine from their shape (and also from the cell width) whether a male **(2)** or a worker will hatch out of the cell. The cap of a cell housing a future worker is flat; male cells have convex caps. The future queen develops in a large queen cell **(1)**. After the queen has hatched, the workers remove this cell.

The queen's development takes the shortest time, only 15—16 days. The worker's development takes 21 days. The development of the male takes three days longer than that of the worker.

The queen lives about 4 to 5 years but older queens have been recorded. Summer workers only live about 4—5 weeks. The male's life is also short.

The worker bees go through a number of 'jobs' during their short lives. Their lives can be roughly divided into three main periods. Each of these is dominated by an activity which depends on the development or disappearance of pharyngeal glands in the head and wax-forming glands in the abdomen. Both the pharyngeal and wax-forming glands are only active at certain times during the bee's lifetime. The individual's working periods are not strictly delineated for the bee can help out where it is needed, even though it ought to be attending to other 'work' at the time. The first job is as a house bee, where the bee works as a cleaner for about three days. Straight after hatching it cleans its own hairs and then the cells in the comb. Then it is its task to look after the larvae. Its pharyngeal glands begin to produce a very nourishing secretion which is fed to the larvae. The larvae of future queens and the queen herself take only this very nutritious food throughout their lives. The older larvae are fed pollen and nectar. Towards the end of this first period the worker begins to make orientation flights in the immediate neighbourhood of the hive.

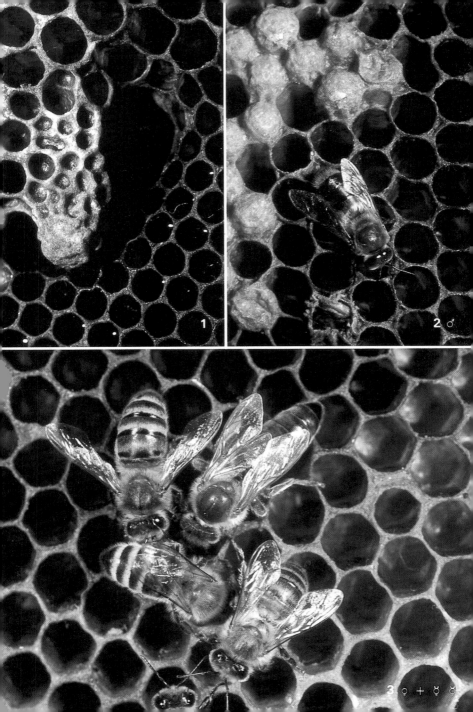

1

2 ♂

3 ♀ + ☿ ♂

Family: Apidae — Honeybees and Bumblebees

⊗ *Apis mellifera* L. — Honeybee (continued). In the second period of the worker's life, building work predominates. It is a time when its pharyngeal glands regress and its abdominal wax-producing glands become fully functional. As well as building work there are other tasks to be done: the bees thicken the nectar in the cells and also compress the pollen with their heads. The bee spends a short period around the 20th day of its life as a guard. It remains inside the entrance (in the vestibule) and ensures that no strange bees or various bee thieves (e.g. wasps or Hornets) get in.

After this short service, the third and last period of the bee's life begins: it becomes a forager (1). By now its life is nearly over. The wax-producing glands have atrophied and its main duty now is to gather pollen and nectar. It gathers pollen with its mandibles and specially adapted brushes on its legs (2). On its hind legs pollen baskets have developed (i.e. a hollow in the tibia flanked by brushes of long hairs). With the help of these brushes the bee scrapes the pollen caught on its body hairs into the baskets and carries it back to the hive. It sucks up the nectar with its long tongue.

The bee has the ability to distinguish colours. Blue and yellow are the colours it sees best. Unlike the human eye, the bee's eye is not very sensitive to red (it perceives it as dark grey) but it is very sensitive to ultraviolet radiation. This colour preference is used by the beekeeper in the choice of the colour for the front of the hive. The bee also has its own language, expressed by dancing. We owe the deciphering of this mysterious way of bee communication to Professor K. von Frisch, the Nobel Prize winner, and his team. With the help of various dances, the foragers can not only inform their sisters about the direction in which to fly to the discovered food source, but also transmit further data about its distance from the hive and its quality.

The bee colony is not an unchanging unit. At a certain time the bees swarm. This is a way of separating off a part of the colony from the original nest. The flight takes place at a time when the young queens in the queen cells are ready to hatch. The old queen — the original founder of the nest — flies out of the hive with about half of the bees and vacates it to make way for a young queen. The swarm usually hangs from a tree branch. Just as the foraging workers are able to pass on information about food sources, the scouts are able to transmit information about places suitable for settling. The beekeeper usually anticipates this, shakes the swarm off into a box and transfers in into a new hive. In this way not only are the bees spared the problems connected with choosing a suitable nesting site, but also those of building the nest. Meanwhile, several basic changes take place in the original colony. The young queen which was the first to hatch, destroys the queens in all the other queen cells. After mating she starts laying eggs and the colony's life continues. The colonies of wasps and bumblebees last only one year. The Honeybee colony lives for several years. The bees overwinter in a multi-layered cluster with the queen concealed in the middle. Inside this cluster a temperature of between 20 and 36 °C is maintained; the temperature on the outside of the cluster does not drop below 10 °C. With the new spring the colony awakens again. The worker bees are among the first insects to be seen on the early spring flowers.

1 ☿

2

Family: Apidae — Honeybees and Bumblebees

⊗ ***Bombus pascuorum*** (Scop.) — Common Carder Bee — is also known as *B. agrorum* (F.). It belongs to the sub-genus *Thoracobombus*. It lives in a variety of habitats, both dry and damp — in meadows, parks, gardens, woods and fields. It occurs mainly in the lowland and foothill regions; it does inhabit the upland pine forests but is less common there. It is one of the most common bumblebees or humblebees. The length of its head is greater than its width. Many colour forms have been recorded in its extensive distribution; these are mostly related to the variable colour of the abdomen. The basic coloration of females **(1)**, workers and males **(2)** in central Europe is as follows: the head is covered with yellowish hair, the thorax with orange-yellow hair (in some individuals there is a triangular group of black hairs in the middle of the thorax) and the abdomen with yellowish and yellowish-grey hair. Only the second and third abdominal segments are covered with black hairs. The farther north one goes, the darker are the individuals. A reliable identifying feature of this species is the orange hair on the thorax.

Like all European bumblebees, *B. pascuorum* lives socially in a colony throughout its life. Like wasps, bumblebees are unable to accumulate enough food before the arrival of winter and therefore the workers, males and the old queen, which founded the nest in the spring, all die in the autumn. Only the young mated females, reared at the end of the summer before the demise of the colony, hibernate over winter and in the spring found new nests. The queen leaves her winter quarters in the spring, most often in the second half of April (this depends on the weather). She is hungry and weak after many months of winter fast. For several days she flies from flower to flower, sucking nectar and sunning herself. Only then does she begin to search for a suitable site for a nest. She is very flexible in her choice of location. Sometimes she builds her nest in grass, moss or leaves, in a clover field; at other times in a deserted bird's nest (even high up a tree), in a squirrel's drey etc. She often nests in the immediate vicinity of man — in cowsheds, barns, the wooden walls of houses, even in a bucket of old rags, and in old, unused eiderdowns, etc.

The nest is small, containing only about 100 to 200 cells. As soon as the female discovers a suitable site, she returns to it again and again in order to fix its position in her memory. From this moment the fate of the future colony depends on her. Many females (50 per cent or more) perish soon after founding their nest due to inclement weather; this means the end of the entire colony. The architectural art of the bumblebee is not of the highest order. If we compare its creations with those of bees or wasps, the bumblebee remains far behind.
Length ⚥ 14—16 mm, ♀ 18—22 mm, ♂ 13—18 mm.

1 ♀

2 ♂

Family: Apidae — Honeybees and Bumblebees

⊙ *Bombus pascuorum* (Scop.) — Common Carder Bee (continued). The female (2) carries a supply of pollen into the nest (2) as food for the larvae and stores it in a wax pot or cell, about 5 mm in diameter. She lays her eggs on this pollen (usually eight of them); there are two eggs in the middle row and three in each of the neighbouring rows. Then the female covers this formation with a layer of wax and begins to build a cup-like structure of wax near the nest entrance. This cup is placed about 12—18 mm from the egg cell and she fills it with nectar which serves as her food store in bad weather. After founding the nest, the female is exhausted. She has had to look after herself, gather provisions for the nest, warm the egg cell (and later the larvae) with her body and feed the larvae.

The development is relatively quick; the female needs helpers because she could not service the growing nest by herself. The larvae are white, grub-like, legless and fast-growing. The full-grown larva secretes silk, which solidifies rapidly to form a fibre. With this the larva spins a cocoon with thin but very strong walls. The cocoons resemble hazelnuts. The larva pupates in the cocoon and after a short interval the adult hatches out. The first offspring are always workers — females with imperfectly developed ovaries. They are very small because they received only the bare minimum of food during their development. After hatching they eat their fill from the nest stores and after several days they begin flying out to gather nectar and pollen. The female makes other pollen plates and continues to lay eggs. The nest grows in numbers; at the height of summer males and females begin to appear. The males gradually develop from unfertilized eggs. They are slimmer than the females but the workers do not drive them out of the nest. They fly out on their own, at first returning at night but later staying out of doors on flowers. On fine October days they can still be found on flowering thistles, which are sought after by various bumblebee species during late autumn.

Both the workers and the females have a long sting. However, they are not aggressive and only sting in self-defence; their sting, unlike that of a Honeybee, does not remain in the wound. The males have no sting. Along with other bumblebee species, *B. pascuorum* is important as a clover pollinator. In the spring it occurs on flowering narcissi in gardens, on wood anemones, lungwort and later blackberry flowers in woods. In the summer it can be commonly seen on thyme, sage, etc. It also frequents foxgloves, snowberry bushes, deadnettles, willows, St. John's Wort and Greater Celandine.

B. pascuorum occurs throughout Europe, including the north, Siberia, the Caucasus, Turkestan, etc.

Family: Apidae — Honeybees and Bumblebees

⊗ **Bombus pomorum** (PANZ.) There is a great deal of colour variation in this species. Typical individuals are covered in black hair, only on the tergites — third to sixth in females and workers, third to seventh in males — does the hair have a reddish tinge. *B. pomorum* **(1)** could be easily mistaken for several similarly coloured species, e.g. *B. lapidarius* (L.), *B. ruderarius* (MÜLL.) or *B. mastrucatus* GERST. Thus, as well as coloration, we also have to consider other features in order to separate these species.

B. pomorum occurs most commonly in warm wooded regions, especially in the lowlands; it is only occasionally found in mountainous terrain (up to 2,000 m). It inhabits meadows, fields, gardens and woods. The females appear after hibernation in late April and May. Their nest is always underground, e.g. in vole nests, in hedgerows, etc. The entrance is masked by dry grass under which the nest guards are hidden. *B. pomorum* seeks out plants of the families Labiatae and Compositae. Along with several other bumblebee species, *B. pomorum* is important as a pollinator of clover.

It is widespread in Europe, except in the north and south. In the Alps it is found up to 1,800 m. It also occurs in Siberia.

Length ☿, ♀ 20—24 mm, ♂ 18—20 mm.

⊙ **Bombus subterraneus** (L.) — Short-haired Bumblebee — inhabits places up to 800 m above sea level. The females fly in May after hibernation and make their nests underground. The males **(2)** appear in August. Among the favourite food plants of this species are clover, deadnettles and thistles.

B. subterraneus occurs throughout Eurasia.

Length ☿, ♀ 17—30 mm, ♂ 15—20 mm.

⊗ **Bombus hortorum** (L.) — Large Garden Bumblebee. As in other bumblebees, the coloration of this species is also variable. The most frequent form is covered with black hairs. The female **(3)** has yellow hairs on the pronotum, the scutellum and on the first and the front edge of the second abdominal tergites. The hairs are white on the fourth and fifth tergites. In the male the sixth tergite is black in the centre but covered with white hairs laterally. The yellow band on the male's scutellum is indented at the front.

This species has a conspicuously long head. Moreover, this bumblebee has the longest tongue of all central European species (as long as the length of the body). Thus it can pollinate plants which neither honeybees nor other bumblebee species are able to. It occurs on the edges of woods and in scrubby areas on both low ground and in the mountains (it reaches altitudes of 2,000 m). The overwintered females appear in early spring. They found their nests in enclosed spaces, usually underground, but sometimes in houses (in old rags, under floors), etc. This bumblebee is easily cultivated in man-made hives. There are about 300—400 individuals in each nest. *B. hortorum* is an important pollinator of clover and fruit trees. It also frequents foxgloves, deadnettle, lungwort, cowslips and many other plants. The males fly in August and can be found on flowers until October.

B. hortorum inhabits all of Europe and temperate Asia (Siberia, Mongolia).

Length ☿, ♀ 20—24 mm, ♂ 18—20 mm.

1

2 ♂

3 ♀

Family: Apidae — Honeybees and Bumblebees

⊗ *Bombus lapidarius* (L.) — Large Red-tailed Bumblebee — is one of the most conspicuous and most common central European bumblebee species. It is covered with black hairs; only the last few abdominal segments bear red hairs. In the male (2) the clypeus and pronotum are yellow-haired. However, several other central European species share this coloration, e.g. *B. mastrucatus, B. ruderarius* and *B. pomorum. B. lapidarius* flies in woods, fields, meadows, gardens and the females sometimes fly into houses in their search for a nesting site.

The females (3) appear in the spring. Hungry after their long hibernation, their first job is to look for food — the nectar and pollen of spring flowers. Only after feeding do they begin to search for suitable nesting places. The female slowly flies low over the ground, often landing and crawling into various cavities in order to examine them. She also explores piles of stones and sometimes cracks in the walls of country houses. She is not very selective in her choice of site. Once she has selected a suitable place, she begins to arrange the nest; she lines it with moss and dry plants. She then stores a pollen mass in a wax cup and lays several eggs on it. She also constructs a wax cup where she stores nectar. The development is similar to that of other bumblebees. Workers (1) sometimes show cannibalism — they attempt to steal the queen's eggs and eat them. The queen chases them off. The workers' life is relatively short — only about 5 weeks. The bumblebees return to their nest for the night; the nest is usually awake even at night. A medium-sized nest of *B. lapidarius* has about 300 individuals.

The mated females, which hatched in late summer, feed voraciously in the autumn before looking for a suitable place in which to hibernate. They burrow about 15 centimetres underground under hedgerows, into wooded slopes, etc. In the earth they make a chamber which becomes their home for the next few months.

B. lapidarius is an important pollinator of long trumpet-shaped flowers, as are other bumblebee species. They are important pollinators of flowers the honeybees cannot reach into with their shorter tongues. Along with *B. pascuorum, B. hortorum* and other species, *B. lapidarius* is an important clover pollinator. It frequents also flowering blackberry, various Boraginaceae, Larkspur, dandelions, thistles and other plants.

It inhabits a large part of Europe, extending in the north up to Lapland. In the Alps it is found up to 2,000 m. Like other bumblebee species, *B. lapidarius* is protected by law in parts of Europe.

Length ☿, ♀ 24—27 mm, ♂ 14—18 mm.

1 ⚥

2 ♂

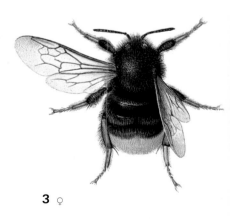

3 ♀

Family: Apidae — Honeybees and Bumblebees

⊗ **Bombus muscorum** (L.) — Moss Carder Bee **(1)** — is consistent in its colouring: it is covered with yellowish-brown hair. It inhabits fields and meadows throughout the lowlands and foothills (in the Alps up to 800 m). The overwintered females appear in late April and May. They establish surface nests without protective coverings, most often in a tuft of grass or in moss. Their nests have also been found in old squirrels' dreys. The numbers of their inhabitants are low — only several dozen. *B. muscorum* can often be seen on various plants of the Boraginaceae family, oxtongue, etc. It also frequents cover fields. The males fly out of the nests from August and can be seen on flowers as late as October. *B. muscorum* is one of the rarer species of bumblebee.

It occurs over a large part of Europe, with the exception of the north and the south. It is also found in northern Asia.

Length ☿, ♀ 18—22 mm, ♂ 13—16 mm.

⊗ **Bombus ruderarius** (MÜLL.) — Knapweed Carder Bee — is very variable in coloration. The basic male, female and worker coloration is as follows: the body is covered with black hair; only the last few abdominal segments have reddish hair **(2)**. At a glance, it could be mistaken for several similarly coloured species. *B. ruderarius* lives in meadows, gardens and fields. The overwintered females fly in mid-April (in May in higher localities) and feed on the flowers of cowslips, larkspur, crocuses etc. They establish their nests on the surface, often in hollows overgrown with grass and moss, and do not cover them with a protective ceiling. The nest is about 25—30 centimetres high. The workers hatch in mid-June. They seek out the flowers of various plants of the families Boraginaceae, Labiatae and Asteraceae. They are also important clover pollinators. The males appear in July and August.

B. ruderarius inhabits Europe, except for the far north and south. In the Alps it is found up to 2,200 m.

Length ☿, ♀ 16—20 mm, ♂ 15—18 mm.

⊗ **Bombus silvarum** (L.) **(3)** is relatively constant in coloration, unlike many other species. It occurs especially in oak woods (it is rare in coniferous woods), in fields, meadows and gardens. The females leave their winter quarters in April and May, depending on the weather and the location. The nest is either above ground or underground and is built in deserted vole or mole burrows, uncovered birds' nests or squirrels' dreys. The nest is not very large — it contains only several dozen individuals. The female sometimes eats her own eggs as do all bumblebee queens when food is scarce or the weather is too cold for flight. The males fly in August and can be found on flowers until the end of September. *B. silvarum* frequents the flowers of deadnettle, sage, scabious, cornflower and thistles, and also pollinates clover.

It inhabits a large part of Europe with the exception of the far north; also northern Asia. In the Alps it is found up to about 1,600 m.

Length ☿, ♀ 18—20 mm, ♂ 15—18 mm.

1

2

3

Family: Apidae — Honeybees and Bumblebees

⊗ **Bombus terrestris** (L.) — Buff-tailed Bumblebee — is one of the most common and most conspicuous European bumblebees. Its coloration is not very variable. It is covered with black hair; the hair on the pronotum and second abdominal tergite is yellow and on the fourth and fifth tergites is it white (distinctly buff in British populations). This coloration strongly resembles that of *B. lucorum* (L.) **(4)** and the two species cannot be distinguished by the naked eye. Their identification is not always easy even for an expert armed with a strong magnifying glass or microscope. The main identifying features of the females and workers **(2)** are the surface sculpture (punctures) on the head and the abdomen and the distance between the ocelli. The males **(1)** can be identified with the additional help of some mandibular and genitalia characters.

B. terrestris occurs in woods, meadows, fields and gardens from lowland to mountainous regions. The young females **(3)** appear in early March. *B. terrestris* belongs to the earliest of the bumblebees; its first food is the nectar of flowering coltsfoot, willows and anemones.

The female makes her nest deep in the ground, in a mouse or mole burrow. There she finds enough dry material for lining her nest — dry grass, leaves and moss. Her nest is often deeper than 1 metre, which is advantageous for such an early bumblebee colony. At this depth it is easier to survive spring frosts which weaken or destroy the colonies of surface-living species in some seasons. The *B. terrestris* nest is as untidy as that of other species. Numerically, it is one of the largest with up to 500 individuals.

In the workers cannibalism sometimes occurs; they attempt to devour the laying queen's eggs. Even the queen will sometimes eat her own eggs. From late July young females and males appear in the nest. The males leave the nest after a certain time and frequent flowering plants until October. The young females burrow into the earth in the autumn to hibernate. They prefer to burrow deep under a tree; the whole operation only takes a few minutes. Sometimes the females overwinter in the nest where they were born and at times they hibernate in groups.

B. terrestris is an important pollinator of various plants. Its significance is the greater for being very common in some localities. It pollinates fruit trees on cold spring days when the honeybees stay in their hives. In mountainous regions it pollinates raspberries, blueberries and red whortleberries. Like other species, *B. terrestris* is also an important clover pollinator. It also pollinates a number of other plant species. Sometimes it bites a hole in the flower, through which it sucks the nectar without pollinating the plant.

It inhabits all Europe, southern Africa and Asia Minor.

Length ☿, ♀ 20—22 mm, ♂ 11—22 mm.

1 ♂ 2 ☿

3 ♀ 4

Family: Apidae — Honeybees and Bumblebees

⊗ **Bombus pratorum** (L.) — Early Bumblebee — is another very variably coloured species. Most individuals are coloured as follows: the pronotum is yellow in both sexes, the fourth to sixth tergites of females and the fifth to seventh and sometimes the fourth tergites of the males are usually covered with red hair. The male **(2)** has a whitish yellow-haired clypeus and a yellow vertex. This bumblebee resembles to a certain extent not only the following species but also B. lapidarius and other species.

B. pratorum is common in woods in both lowland and mountainous regions (in the Alps it extends up to 2,500 m). The young females **(1)** emerge from hibernation in early spring. Depending on the weather, they appear as early as late March and early April, together with the other two early species — B. terrestris and B. hortorum. They sit on sallow catkins and gather and eat pollen. They also seek out flowering hellebore, cowslips, lungwort, larkspur, etc.

The female makes her nest in various places, sometimes on the surface — under moss or in a thicket, sometimes underground (e.g. in a deserted mouse hole or under the floor of a country barn). She also builds them in hollow trees, in deserted birds' nests and squirrels' dreys. The workers appear from June to September, the males and young females fly from late June and early July onwards. During the summer this bumblebee can be seen on Rosaceae (including fruit trees), Labiatae, Boraginaceae and Asteraceae.

B. pratorum is widespread over all Europe and northern Asia.
Length ☿, ♀ 16—21mm, ♂ 11—16 mm.

⊙ **Bombus mastrucatus** GERST. has a conspicuously broad head **(3)**. It is as variable in coloration as the preceding species which it resembles. It is covered with black hair; in the females and workers the fourth to sixth abdominal tergites and in the males the fourth to seventh tergites are red. The male clypeus is covered with yellow hair, as are the vertex, pronotum and sometimes also the scutellum.

B. mastrucatus is a mountain and foothill species; it was first described in the Alps more than a century ago. In some places, especially in coniferous woodland, it is very common. The overwintered females emerge from hibernation relatively late. They fly at the time when the blueberries are flowering. The female builds her nest exclusively underground and her colony is usually very numerous, with several hundred individuals.

B. mastrucatus visits a large number of flowering plants of various species. To penetrate to the food source more easily, it sometimes bites a hole in the flower, through which it sucks the nectar. It is commonly found on cowslips, blueberries, sage, monkshood, foxgloves but also vetches, thistles and many other species. It also pollinates clover.

It is widespread in the mountainous and foothill regions of Europe from the Pyrenees to the Balkans and as far north as Scandinavia.
Length ☿, ♀ 20—26 mm, ♂ 13—18 mm.

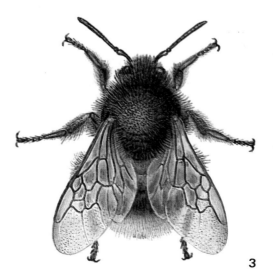

1 ♀

2 ♂

3

Family: Apidae — Honeybees and Bumblebees

⊗ **Psithyrus campestris** (PANZ.) — Field Cuckoobee — can be variable in coloration and resembles several other bumblebee species. Its thorax and abdomen is, however, more shiny than those of bumblebees and its wings are dark. It is difficult to distinguish a male of the *Psithyrus* species from a bumblebee male; indeed, it is often impossible without examining the copulatory organs. The female can best be identified by the absence of the pollen-gathering apparatus on her hind legs and her abdomen being more curved. She also lacks wax-producing glands which exude the tiny scales of wax.

Unlike the bumblebees, *Psithyrus* have no worker caste. Their females cannot find their own nesting sites and found nests. Therefore they pass on the task of feeding and bringing up their larvae to involuntary hosts.

The overwintered females appear on flowers in May and June. Their first interest is to eat their fill of nectar and pollen. As they cannot scrape the pollen off their bodies into pollen baskets, it remains stuck to their body hair. After a certain time, the female begins to search for a suitable bumblebee nest where her larvae develop. She usually chooses the nests of *Bombus pascuorum, B. pomorum* or *B. subterraneus* and invades the nest at a time when the first workers have already hatched. In most cases she is accepted and crawls among the nest cells where her body becomes permeated by the nest odour. Then she lays her eggs in cells prepared for bumblebee eggs. The host workers devote the same attention to her larvae as they do to their own. The *Psithyrus* larvae pupate in the cells and in late summer males and females hatch from the pupae. The males **(1)** are common on various thistles and other plants during September.

P. campestris lives in Europe and temperate Asia.
Length ♀ 15—17 mm, ♂ 11—16 mm.

⊗ **Psithyrus bohemicus** (SEIDL) — Gipsy Cuckoobee — occurs in various colour forms. The overwintered females **(2)** appear in May and June. They can commonly be seen on clover, common melilot, etc. The female invades the nests of *Bombus lucorum,* where she lays her eggs and the next generation of *Psithyrus bohemicus* develops. The males occur on various plants of the family Asteraceae from July and the females appear in August.

P. bohemicus is widespread through the Palaearctic region.
Length ♀ 14—20 mm, ♂ 12—18 mm.

⊗ **Psithyrus rupestris** (F.) — Hill Cuckoobee — resembles in colouring *Bombus lapidarius* in whose nests it lives and whose workers bring up its larvae. The robust female **(3, 4)** has dark brown wings and her last abdominal tergites are covered with red hair. She flies in May and June in clover fields and on the edges of woods, where she searches for a host nest. The new generation appears in late summer. The males occur commonly on various thistles from August onwards. The young females hibernate.

P. rupestris is widespread in central and southern Europe.
Length ♀ 18—25 mm, ♂ 10—18 mm.

1 ♂

2 ♀

3 ♀

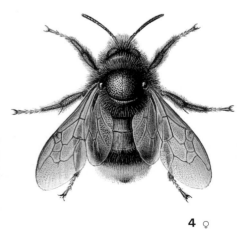

4 ♀

BIBLIOGRAPHY

Alford, D. V.
  Bumblebees (London, 1975)

Andrewes, C. H.
  The Lives of Wasps and Bees (1969)

Beiderbeck, R. and Koefoet, J.
  Pflanzengallen am Wegesrand (Stuttgart, 1979)

Chinery, M.
  Collins Guide to the Insects of Britain and Western Europe
  (London, 1986)

Darlington, A.
  The Pocket Encyclopedia of Plant Galls in Colour (London, 1968)

Donisthorpe, H. StJ. K.
  British Ants, their Life History and Classification (London, 1927)

Edwards, R.
  Social Wasps. Their Biology and Control (West Sussex, 1980)

Evans, H. E.
  The Comparative Ethology and Evolution of the Sand Wasps
  (1966)

Frisch, K. von
  The Dance Language and Orientation of Bees (Oxford, 1968)

Lindauer, M.
  Communication among Social Bees, 3rd ed. (1971)

Larson, P. D. and Larson, M. W.
  Lives of Social Insects (New York, 1968)

Plateau-Quenu, C.
  La Biologie des Abeilles Primitives (Paris, 1972)

Ribbands, C. R.
  The Behaviour and Social Life of Honeybees (1953)

Richards, O. W.
  The Social Insects (London, 1953)

Royal Entomological Society
  Handbooks for the Identification of British Insects
    Vol. 6, Pt 2C, Sect. 3 **Hymenoptera: Symphyta** (R. B. Benson,
      London, 1959)
    Vol. 6, Pt 3B **Scolioidea, Vespoidea and Sphecoidea**
      (O. W. Richards, London, 1980)

Vol. 7, Pt 2, Sect. 1 **Hymenoptera: Ichneumonoidea**
(J. F. Perkins, London, 1959)

Vol. 7, Pt 2A, Sect. 2 **Hymenoptera: Ichneumonoidea**
(J. F. Perkins, London, 1960)

Vol. 8, Pt 1A **Hymenoptera: Cynipoidea** (R. D. Eady and
J. Quinlan, London, 1960)

Vol. 8, Pt 2A **Hymenoptera: Chalcidoidea** (G. J. Kerrich, London,
1958)

Vol. 8, Pt B **Hymenoptera: Chalcidoidea** (R. R. Askew, London,
1968)

Vol. 8, Pt 3B **Hymenoptera: Proctotrupoidea** (G. E. J. Nixon,
London, 1967)

Wheeler, W. M.
Ants: Their Structure, Development and Behaviour (1910)
The Social Insects: Their Origin and Evolution (1928)

Wilson, E. O.
The Insect Societies (Cambridge, Mass., 1971)

INDEX